FIRST AID IN ENGLISH

READER

by

A. MACIVER

D1610624

BOOK
F

ROBERT GIBSON & SONS, Glasgow, LIMITED
17 FITZROY PLACE   :   GLASGOW

Books by
ANGUS MACIVER

FIRST AID IN ENGLISH
NEW FIRST AID IN ENGLISH

CONCISE FIRST AID IN ENGLISH
Edited by D.A. MacLennan, M.A.

READERS

READER A
READER B
READER C
READER D
READER E
READER F

**The information in this edition
is correct to February 1989.**

ISBN 0 7169 5505 9

Printed in Great Britain by Bell and Bain Ltd., Glasgow

1. CORACIUS CAUDATUS (Lilac-breasted Roller). 2. MEROPS NUBICOIDES (Carmine Bee Eater).
3. ORIOLUS NOTATUS PETERS (South African Golden Oriole). 4. IMPALA.
5. BUSHBUCK DOE. 6. HARE. 7. ZEBRA. 8. YOUNG MONKEYS.
9. ACACIA SERICOCEPHALA FENAL (Albiggia).

" Interest is the soil in which Intelligence and Knowledge grow."

PREFACE

In earlier stages of reading, emphasis has been placed on the mechanics of diction and the attainment of an adequate speed of recital. At this stage, the most important needs are to understand fully what is read and to acquire a taste for reading. To ensure the necessary concentration, **the stories in these books are specially selected to arouse, maintain, and satisfy the interest of the pupils.** The short paragraphs of Interesting Facts have a direct bearing on the stories, either by subject or scene, and should help considerably in the change from **learning to read** to **reading to learn.** The Questions on both Stories and Facts are **in sequence** and demand not only that the pupils read carefully but also that they remember the salient points. The answers (oral or written) can be used as **a direct aid to Composition.** The Development Exercises endeavour to expand on certain statements in the matter read, and the questions are designed to give the pupils an opportunity to express their thoughts and knowledge, simply and accurately.

These Readers are complementary to " First Aid in English," and therefore needless repetition, in language study and correct usage, has been purposely avoided.

A. M.

ACKNOWLEDGMENTS

We value highly the permission to include copyright material and are happy to put on record our indebtedness for the following extracts:

THE WOLF TEST from *Warrior Scarlet* by Rosemary Sutcliff to the Author and Oxford University Press.

THE CATTLE STAMPEDE from *Tramp Royal* by Sir Michael Bruce to the Author and Elek Books Ltd.

THE CAVALIER'S ESCAPE by G. W. Thornbury from *The Laurel and Gold* Book of Verse to the Author and Messrs. Wm. Collins, Sons and Co. Ltd.

A NORSE SAGA from *The Heroes of Asgard* by A. and E. Keary to the Authors and Messrs. Macmillan & Co. Ltd.

THE VIRTUOUS ONE from *The Small Woman* by Alan Burgess to the Author and Messrs. Evans Brothers Ltd.

THE CONQUEST OF EVEREST from *The Ascent of Everest* by Col. Sir John Hunt to the Author and Messrs. Hodder & Stoughton Ltd.

A JAPANESE LEGEND from *The Children's Encyclopedia* edited by Arthur Mee to Fleetway Publications Ltd.

THE OLD GREY SQUIRREL from *You and Your World* by Alfred Noyes to the Author's executors.

KARIBA from *Operation Noah* by Charles Lagus to the Author and Messrs. Wm. Kimber & Co. Ltd.

THE SPECTACLED ROADMAN from *The Thirty-Nine Steps* by John Buchan to the Author's trustees and Messrs. Wm. Blackwood & Sons Ltd.

THE CYCLONE from *The Cruise of the Cachalot* by Frank T. Bullen to Messrs. John Murray Publishers Ltd.

THE YOUNG POET from *Young Walter Scott* by E. J. Gray to the Author, the Viking Press Inc. and Penguin Books Ltd.

and for permission to reproduce the photograph of the Kariba Dam on page 200, to The High Commissioner for Rhodesia and Nyasaland,

and for the photograph of Luichart Dam on page 207, to The North of Scotland Hydro-Electric Board

We express our thanks also to The British Red Cross Society for their courtesy and help in preparing the chapter on The Red Cross

CONTENTS

MISSION FOR THE QUEEN

The weak French King Louis XIII mistrusted his Queen because of her friendship with the English ambassador, the Duke of Buckingham. In order to discredit the Queen even more, Cardinal Richelieu, the most powerful man in France, asked the King to arrange a ball in Paris, at which her Majesty would wear the diamond studs which she had received from the King on her birthday. Richelieu, through his spies, was well aware that the Queen had already given the diamond studs to Buckingham as a keepsake.

In this extract from "The Three Musketeers" by Alexandre Dumas, the gallant D'Artagnan, with the three musketeers Athos, Porthos and Aramis, sets out for London to bring back the diamond studs in time for the ball.

AT two o'clock in the morning our four adventurers, followed by their lackeys, left Paris by the gate St. Denis.

All went well as far as Chantilly, where they stopped for breakfast at an inn recommended by a sign showing St. Martin giving half his cloak to a poor man.

A gentleman also sat having breakfast at the same table. When the comrades rose to depart, the stranger proposed to Porthos to drink the Cardinal's health. Porthos replied that he desired nothing better, if the stranger in his turn would drink the King's health. The stranger cried that he acknowledged no other king but his Eminence. Porthos told him he was drunk and the stranger drew his sword.

"You have committed a piece of folly," said Athos, "but it can't be helped. Kill your man and rejoin us as soon as you can." All three mounted their horses and departed at full speed whilst Porthos promised his adversary to perforate him in all the fashions known to the fencing school.

At Beauvais they stopped, as much to breathe their horses as to wait for Porthos. At the end of two hours, as Porthos did not come, they resumed their journey.

About a league from Beauvais, where the road was confined between two high banks, they fell in with eight or ten men, who appeared to be employed digging holes. The labourers drew back to the ditch, from which each took a concealed musket. The result was that our seven travellers were outnumbered in weapons. Aramis received a ball which passed through his shoulder and Mousqueton, Porthos' lackey, was hit by a ball which knocked him from his horse.

"It is an ambuscade!" shouted D'Artagnan; "don't waste a shot! Forward!"

Aramis, wounded as he was, seized the mane of his horse which carried him off with the others.

At Crevecoeur, Aramis declared that he could not go on. He grew paler every minute and they were obliged to support him on his horse. They lifted him off at the door of an inn, left his servant Bazin with him and set forward again in the hope of reaching Amiens and passing the night there. They arrived at midnight and alighted at the inn of the Golden Lily.

The host had the appearance of as honest a man as any on earth. He received the travellers with his candlestick in one hand and his cotton nightcap in the other.

"Grimaud can take care of the horses," said Planchet. "I will sleep across your doorway and you will be certain that nobody can come to you."

At four o'clock in the morning, a terrible noise was heard in the stables. Grimaud had tried to waken the stable-boys, and the stable-boys were beating him. When the window was opened, the poor lad was lying senseless from a blow with a fork-handle, and the horses were completely foundered.

This began to be annoying. All these successive accidents were perhaps the result of chance, but they might, quite as probably be the fruits of a plot. Planchet was sent to inquire if there were three horses for sale in the neighbourhood. At the door stood two horses, fresh, strong and fully equipped. This was just the thing. He asked where their owners were, and was informed that they had passed the night in the inn, and were then settling with the master.

When Athos went down to pay the reckoning, four men, armed to the teeth, entered by side-doors and rushed upon him. "I am taken!" shouted Athos, with all the power of his lungs. "Go on, D'Artagnan! Spur! Spur!" And he fired two pistols.

D'Artagnan and Planchet, who were standing at the street door, did not wait to be twice warned. They unfastened the two horses, leaped upon them and set off at full gallop for St. Omer and from thence to Calais.

At a hundred paces from the gates of Calais. D'Artagnan's horse sank under him while Planchet's mount stopped short and could by no means be got up again. They left their horses upon the highway and ran towards the port. Planchet called his master's attention to a gentleman in front who had just arrived with his lackey.

They hastily drew near this gentleman, who appeared to be in a great hurry. His boots were covered with dust and he was asking whether he could not instantly cross over to England.

"Nothing would be more easy," said the captain of a vessel ready to sail, "but this morning an order arrived that no one should be allowed to cross without express permission from the Cardinal."

"I have that permission," said the gentleman, drawing a paper from his pocket. "Here it is."

"Have it signed by the governor of the port," said the captain "and give me the preference."

"Very well," said the gentleman and with his lackey, he started for the governor's house.

D'Artagnan and Planchet followed the gentleman at a distance of five hundred yards. Once outside the city however, D'Artagnan quickly overtook the gentleman as he was entering a little wood.

"Planchet," called out D'Artagnan, "take care of the lackey. I will manage the master."

Planchet, being strong and vigorous, soon had his opponent on his back and he placed his knee on his chest.

"Go on with your affair, sir," cried Planchet, "I have finished mine," And he bound and gagged his unfortunate victim.

Meanwhile the gentleman had drawn his sword and had sprung upon D'Artagnan. In three seconds D'Artagnan had wounded him three times, exclaiming at each thrust, "One for Athos! One for Porthos! And one for Aramis!"

With the fourth thrust, the gentleman closed his eyes and fainted. D'Artagnan searched his pockets and soon found the order for the passage. It was in the name of the Comte de Wardes.

"And now," said D'Artagnan, "to the governor's house."

The governor signed the passport and delivered it to D'Artagnan, who lost no time in useless compliments, but thanked the governor, bowed and departed.

Once out, he and Planchet set off as fast as they could and re-entered the city by another gate. The vessel was quite ready to sail, and the captain waiting on the wharf.

"Here is my pass signed," said D'Artagnan.

"And that other gentleman?" asked the captain.

"He will not go today," said D'Artagnan.

"In that case we will be gone," said the captain . . .

D'Artagnan did not know London; he did not know one word of English, but he wrote the name of Buckingham on a piece of paper, and everyone to whom he showed it pointed out to him the way to the Duke's palace.

On seeing D'Artagnan, Buckingham cried, "Has any misfortune happened to the Queen?"

"I believe not," said D'Artagnan. "Nevertheless she seems in some great peril from which your Grace alone can rescue her. Here is a letter from her Majesty."

Buckingham broke open the seal and avidly read the contents of the letter.

"Come sir, come!" he said sternly and D'Artagnan followed him through several apartments to a bedchamber, which was at once a miracle of taste and of splendour. From beneath a life-size portrait of the Queen of France Buckingham lifted a casket, and he drew from it a large bow of blue ribbon all sparkling with diamonds.

"Here," he said, "are the precious studs. Take them to the Queen." Suddenly he uttered a terrible cry. "All is lost! Two of the studs are missing—there are but ten of them left!"

"Can you have lost them, milord, or have they been stolen?"

"They have been stolen," replied the Duke, "and it is the Cardinal who has dealt me this blow. See, the ribbons which held them have been cut with scissors."

"Let me reflect," continued the Duke. "The only time I wore these studs was at a ball given by the King a week ago at Windsor. The Comtesse de Winter, with whom I had had a quarrel, became reconciled to me, at that ball. The woman is an agent of the Cardinal's."

To D'Artagnan he added, "The ball does not take place till next Monday. Five days yet. That's more time than we need."

The Duke summoned his secretary and his jeweller. To the former he gave a written order for the Lord Chancellor, and to the latter he gave a commission for two diamond studs to be made exactly like the ones on the blue ribbon.

An hour later the ordinance was published in London that no vessel bound for France should leave the ports—not even the packet-boat with letters.

On the day after the next, the two diamond studs were finished. They were such exact imitations that Buckingham could not tell the new ones from the old ones. He immediately called D'Artagnan.

"Here," he said, "are the diamond studs that you came to fetch. Leave the casket with me. You will say that I preserve it."

"I will perform your commission word for word, milord."

"Now, go to the port, ask for the brig 'Sund', and give this letter to the captain. He will convey you to a little port where certainly no one is on the watch for you."

D'Artagnan bowed to the Duke and quickly made his way to the port opposite the Tower of London. He found the vessel that had been named to him, delivered his letter to the captain, who, after having it signed by the warden of the port, set sail at once. The next day he landed at St. Valery. Four hours later he was at Neufchatel. At Pontoise he changed his horse for the last time and he galloped the rest of the journey to Paris.

The next day nothing was talked of in Paris but the ball which the provosts of the city were to give to the King and Queen.

At midnight great cries and loud acclamations were heard. It was the King passing through the streets which led from the Louvre to the City Hall and which were all illuminated with coloured lanterns.

The King was the first to arrive. He was attired in a most elegant hunting costume; when he was thus clothed, he really appeared the first gentleman of his kingdom.

The Cardinal drew near to the King and placed a casket in his hand. The King opened it, and found in it two diamond studs.

"What does this mean?" demanded he of the Cardinal.

"Nothing," replied the latter; "only, if the Queen has the studs—but I very much doubt if she has—count them, sire. If you find only ten, ask her Majesty who can have stolen from her the studs that are here."

The King looked at the Cardinal but had no time to put any question to him. A cry of admiration burst from every mouth. If the King appeared to be the first gentleman of his kingdom, the Queen was assuredly the most beautiful woman in France.

Her huntress habit was admirably becoming. She wore a beaver hat with blue feathers, a *surtout* of pearl-grey velvet fastened with diamond clasps, and a petticoat of blue satin embroidered in silver. On her left shoulder sparkled the diamond studs on a bow of the same colour as the plumes and the petticoat.

The King trembled with joy and the Cardinal with vexation. The Queen had the studs; the only question was, had she ten or twelve? The King left his company and hastened to the Queen.

"I thank you, madame," said he, "for the deference you have shown to my wishes; but I think two of your studs are missing, and I bring them back to you."

At these words he held out to the Queen the two studs the Cardinal had given him.

"How sire?" cried the Queen, affecting surprise; "you are giving me, then, two more. So now I shall have fourteen."

In fact the King counted them and the twelve studs were all on her Majesty's shoulder.

The King called the Cardinal to him.

"What does this mean, Cardinal?" asked the King in a severe tone.

"This means, sire," replied the Cardinal, "that I was desirous of presenting her Majesty with these two studs, and that, not venturing to offer them myself, I adopted this means of inducing her to accept them."

"And I am the more grateful to your Eminence," replied the Queen, with a smile that proved she was not the dupe of this false piece of gallantry, "since I am certain these two studs have cost you as dearly as all the others cost his Majesty."

Then, after bowing to the King and the Cardinal, the Queen returned to her ladies.

[*Adapted.*]

INTERESTING FACTS ABOUT FRANCE
AND THE FRENCH PEOPLE

1. In Roman times, France was called *Gaul*. The country was later invaded by barbarians called "Franks", meaning "fierce men", who gave their name to the country. It is now a *republic*, with a president as its head of state, though up until the Revolution of 1789, kings ruled over France. The patron saint is *Saint Denis*; the country's *tricolour* flag has blue, white and red vertical stripes; the *cock* is the national symbol and the floral emblem is the lily or "fleur-de-lis".

2. At one time France was divided up into little kingdoms and the ruler of one of them, *William, Duke of Normandy* became King of England after defeating the English forces at the battle of Hastings in 1066. Many French words began to appear in the English language, especially in connection with war, art and architecture, law and the church. Later, English territory in France, won largely by the Black Prince, was gradually yielded up, due, in great measure, to the efforts of the famous heroine, Joan of Arc, who was burned at the stake as a witch at Rouen.

3. Each year, the 14th of July is remembered as *Independence Day* and the French people celebrate it with fireworks, music and dancing in the streets. The date denotes the beginning of the *French Revolution* and the capture of the *Bastille*, the notorious Paris prison. During the revolution, the king and queen were executed by means of a grim new machine, which took its name from its inventor, *Dr. Guillotine*. Many of the noble families lost their lives and their possessions during the period known as the Reign of Terror. Under the banner of *"Liberty, Equality and Fraternity"*, the people set up the new republic. The famous national march, *"La Marseillaise"* was composed at this time by Rouget de Lisle.

4. From the ashes of the Revolution rose a great leader, *Napoleon Bonaparte*, who was born in the French island of Corsica in the Mediterranean Sea. Napoleon proved to be a great general and conquered almost the whole of Europe. His defeat by *Lord Nelson* at the famous naval battle of *Trafalgár*, prevented him from invading England. He was decisively defeated by the British and Prussian armies at *Waterloo* in Belgium in 1815, after escaping for "a hundred days" from Elba. He was finally sent in exile to the lonely island of *Saint Helena* in the South Atlantic Ocean, where he died six years later. His body was brought home and he was buried with full military honours in *Les Invalides* museum in Paris.

5. The French have for hundreds of years been the leaders of world *fashion*. The French royal court was the centre of elegance and other countries imitated the styles and customs to be seen there. In recent times, French fashion houses have become world-famous and the most expensive models come from Paris. Buyers from all over the world pay for the privilege of copying these latest styles, and, each year, as fashion changes, fabulous amounts of money are spent in purchasing clothes, ornaments, perfumes and jewellery. Another feature that has brought fame to France is *cooking*. French food and wines are known the world over. From France we get the word "chef" and the menus of the foremost hotels and restaurants in the world are printed in French. Wine is the chief drink, and the products of the French vineyards, champagne, claret and burgundy, are exported to all parts of the world.

6. French weights and measures are based mainly on the *decimal* system. Money is valued in *francs* and *centimes*, with a hundred centimes in each franc. A *metre*, which is the length of a ten millionth part of a line drawn from the Pole to the Equator, is a little more than a yard. A *kilometre*, or a thousand metres, equals about five eighths of a mile. The *gramme* is the unit of weight and, a *kilogramme* or one thousand grammes weighs about two and a quarter pounds. Liquids are measured in *litres* and four and a half litres make almost one gallon.

7. Though France has excelled in many sports, such as football, rugby and tennis, the French are especially enthusiastic for racing. In horse-racing, the *Grand Prix* at the famous Longchamps racecourse is only equalled by the English Derby. The *Tour de France* is a twenty-one day cycle race round the country, and sometimes into neighbouring countries, which starts and ends in Paris. In motorcar racing, speedsters regard the event at *Le Mans* as one of the greatest contests of the motor-racing calendar. The *Monte Carlo Rally* for drivers of ordinary private cars is an outstanding international competition. In this rally drivers begin from various starting points, such as Glasgow, Oslo or Lisbon, and by controlled routes, race to Monte Carlo, on the Riviera.

8. In modern times, many clever French people have contributed to our advancement in knowledge. *Daguerre* perfected the first photographs from 1824-1839 and these daguerreotype pictures were the beginnings of a new field of study which has led to motion pictures and television. *Bleriot* flew the first biplane across the Channel in 1909 and became a pioneer of aviation. *Pasteur* was a doctor who discovered germs and their harmful effects. Milk that has been treated and made free from germs is called "pasteurised milk". *Madame Curie*, though Polish by birth, was a doctor who lived and worked in Paris. She and her husband discovered how radium could be used to treat disease. The Curie Institute is one of the world's greatest cancer research centres. *Bertillon* was the founder of the finger-print system of criminal detection. No two finger-prints in the world are alike. By keeping a library of finger-prints, the police can relate crimes to the suspected persons.

9. In the *Landes*, a swampy district of south-western France, men still walk on stilts to counter the difficulties of walking, just as they have done for centuries. In *Brittany*, where the people come from the same stock as Cornish, Welsh, Irish and Scots people, the old Breton costume is worn. The gay national dress is also worn in *Alsace*, while the *Basque* people of the *Pyrenees*—the mountains which mark the southern frontier with Spain—retain their own special language as well. The district of *Provence*, which includes the sunny *Riviera* shores of *Cannes* and *Nice*, attracts thousands of tourists every year.

10. *Paris* is the centre of national life and the title of "gay Paree" is gained from the numbers of artists, writers and composers who live there, enjoying the carefree pleasures of this beautiful city. The most outstanding building in Paris is the *Eiffel Tower*, built for the Paris Exhibition of 1889 by an engineer *Gustave*

Eiffel, who also made the framework for the statue of Liberty in New York harbour and the locks for the Panama Canal. Other noted buildings include the *Notre Dame Cathedral* built on the original island city in the middle of the River Seine. The *Louvre* contains masterpieces of famous artists and was once the palace of the kings of France. Another royal palace, *Versailles*, witnessed the signing of international peace treaties. The *Arc de Triomphe* is the national war memorial; from its top can be seen the twelve straight avenues that lead to it from all parts of the city. Paris is also the terminus for two famous train routes, the *P.L.M.* (Paris-Lyons-Mediterranean) and the *Orient Express* across Europe, via Vienna and Belgrade to Istanbul.

QUESTIONS ON THE STORY

1. Name the three musketeers.
2. Who had prepared the plot to bring the Queen into disfavour?
3. What mission was given to D'Artagnan and the musketeers?
4. Why was speed essential to their mission?
5. What sign was above the inn where they had breakfast?

6. Tell how Porthos was forced into a fight with a stranger.
7. What happened to Aramis near Beauvais?
8. Write down the names of the lackeys and state to whom each was attached.
9. How was Athos captured?
10. From what port did D'Artagnan intend to cross to England?
11. In what way was the crossing to England made more difficult for D'Artagnan?
12. Tell how D'Artagnan found his way to the Duke's palace.
13. Where did Buckingham keep the diamond studs?
14. How did Buckingham know that two of the studs had been stolen?
15. Who was responsible for stealing them?
16. How did Buckingham manage to replace the diamond studs?
17. Detail the route D'Artagnan took back to Paris.
18. What did Cardinal Richelieu ask the King to do when he gave him the two diamond studs?
19. How did Richelieu manage to explain the two extra studs?
20. What was the Queen's reply to show that she had not been deceived by the Cardinal's gift?

QUESTIONS ON THE INTERESTING FACTS

1. (*a*) What was the old name for France?
   (*b*) How did it get its present name?
2. Name a particular time in history when French words were introduced into the English language.
3. (*a*) Why is the 14th of July celebrated in France?
   (*b*) Who composed the French national anthem?

4. (*a*) Where was Napoleon born?
   (*b*) Why did he not invade England?
   (*c*) Where did he die and where is he buried?
5. (*a*) Name two things for which France is world famous.
   (*b*) Give a reason why restaurants print their menus in French.
6. Give examples of French currency, length, weight and capacity.
7. (*a*) Name two well-known sports meetings in France.
   (*b*) Name two starting points for the Monte Carlo rally.
8. (*a*) Who made the first photographs?
   (*b*) Who is regarded as a pioneer of aviation?
   (*c*) For what was Pasteur famous?
   (*d*) Who discovered that radium could be used to cure disease?
   (*e*) Who was the inventor of the finger-print system?
9. (*a*) Why do the people of Landes walk on stilts?
   (*b*) To what races are the Bretons related?
   (*c*) What range of mountains divides France and Spain?
   (*d*) Name two French towns on the Riviera.
10. (*a*) Name three famous buildings in Paris.
    (*b*) What routes are followed by P.L.M. and the Orient Express?

DEVELOPMENT EXERCISES

1. (*a*) Point out on the map the route followed by the musketeers from Paris to London.
   (*b*) Find out the names of at least three present-day Channel crossings.
   (*c*) Show the route you would follow if you were a driver in the Monte Carlo rally.

2. EITHER *(a)* Give a brief account of how D'Artagnan managed to cross from Calais to England.

   OR   *(b)* If you were in a Paris salon describing a new exclusive model of your own design, tell briefly some of the features you would mention.

3. A musketeer was a soldier who used a musket or gun. Give the meaning of each of the following: *(a)* engineer, *(b)* pioneer, *(c)* privateer, *(d)* auctioneer, *(e)* buccaneer.

4. St. Martin was noted for his charity, in giving to the poor. For what particular quality is each of following saints noted *(a)* St. Francis, *(b)* St. Bernard *(c)* St. George, *(d)* St. Valentine *(e)* St. Nicholas?

5. Make a list of all the titles of people in the story.

6. The Eiffel Tower is associated with Paris. With what towns are the following associated *(a)* Kremlin, *(b)* Leaning Tower, *(c)* Taj Mahal, *(d)* Vatican, *(e)* White House?

7. Write the meaning of each of the following *(a)* French cakes, *(b)* French chalk, *(c)* French leave, *(d)* French polish, *(e)* French window.

8. Many French words and phrases have passed into common English usage, what is the meaning of each of the following: *(a)* aide-de-camp, *(b)* à la carte, *(c)* coiffure, *(d)* nom-de-plume, *(e)* trousseau?

THE WOLF TEST

In her historical novel of the Bronze Age "Warrior Scarlet", Rosemary Sutcliff tells the story of Drem One-arm, a boy with a crippled arm, who, having failed in his manhood test to kill a wolf unaided, receives another chance to be recognised as a Warrior of his Tribe. In this extract, Drem, who had searched the snow-covered hills for Doli, the shepherd, finds him unconscious at the foot of a flint quarry. He sends his hound, Whitethroat, to the village for help.

FROM somewhere ahead of him in the grey murk, it rose; long-drawn, savage, and unutterably sad, the cry of a wolf on the hunting trail. Another cry echoed it, nearer than the first—and then there was only the wind in the silence. Drem felt as though all the blood in his body had jumped back to his heart, and an icy stillness took him. The ewe stirred behind him, snorting and stamping her foot; he prayed that she might not bleat in terror—not that it would make much difference if she did, for the wolves were down wind of them, and the gusts would carry their scent, if indeed the brutes were not running on it already. Something brushed against his knee, and Cu was crouching beside him; he could feel the tremors running through the old dog's body: tremors of fear and fury and hate. He laid his hand for an instant on the dog's neck, and felt the harsh hairs rising against his palm.

Nothing more happened for so long that he felt he could not bear the waiting for a heart-beat longer; he must yell, beat his spear against the chalk, anything to break the thin-drawn agony of waiting. But still he crouched silent, his heart beating with a slow, heavy drub that seemed to wait to listen between each beat, and the old shepherd's hound crouching against his knee. The ewe was snorting again, in pain and terror. She had gone off her feet, and Drem thought she needed help, but he could not help her; not now. The moon swam out suddenly, free of the scudding, curdled cloud into a lake of clear sky—and in the sliding silver light, something moved on the smooth whiteness of the snow before the quarry mouth. Something dark, and running low, like a great hound. But it was no hound; and behind it came two more.

Now that the moment had come it was almost a relief; and as the wolves swerved in their tracks and headed in towards him, Drem began to yell; yell and throw the lumps of chalk that he had gathered. That might frighten

them back for a while, but not for long. If only he had some means of making a fire—fire to singe their hides! The great grey leader flinched from the lump of chalk that caught him on the shoulder, and gave back a little. But they were famine-driven; even in that fitful light Drem could see how their bones stared through their hides; and seeing that there was none against them but one lone shepherd and a dog, they would not be long held from their attack by yelling and lumps of chalk.

They slunk to and fro, dodging the clods he flung at them, and he saw their shining eyes in the moonlight, their lolling tongues and the thick, raised hair of their manes. There was a kind of hideous mirth about them, as though they knew that there could be but one end to the thing, and could afford to laugh.

Already the great grey leader was slinking forward again, his belly almost on the snowy ground, his jaws widening in that obscene grin . . . Drem had no idea how long he had held them off with his lumps of chalk. He had nothing to throw now, except Doli's spear. He caught that up and flung it; but the broad fighting spear was not meant for throwing, and in the uncertain light it did no more than graze the leader's shoulder as it flew. He had nothing left to throw at all now; and the wolves knew it. This was the kill. Drem had caught up his own spear and half risen to his feet, crouching there, his eyes wide and fixed on the oncoming grey

leader. His mouth was very dry. The old hound crouched
snarling at his side, and behind him he was aware, though
he did not know how, that the ewe had struggled to her
feet again, bleating in wild pain and terror.

Nearer and nearer, circling warily, came the grey
leader, squirming and slinking low-bellied over the snow.
In the last moment it seemed to Drem that he had known
this wolf before; and the wolf had known him. The
wicked grin, the welcome in the savage yellow eyes
belonged to a before-time as well as to now. But then
it had been the wolf who waited for the meeting. Now
it was Drem.

Then the great beast gathered himself on his haunches,
and sprang. Drem leapt to meet him, while Cu flung
himself with a snarl at the throat of the second wolf,
the she-wolf. Even as they came together, there was
a distant shout—a burst of shouting—but Drem did not
hear it. In all his world there was only himself and his
wolf, and old Doli; and the ewe struggling to bring
her lamb to birth behind him.

And then not even Doli and the ewe, only himself and his wolf. He had side-slipped as the wolf sprang forward, and his spear took the great brute behind the shoulder and was all but wrenched from his grasp as it turned, yowling, almost in mid-leap. Fiery pain slashed at his right shoulder just as it had done before; but he scarcely felt it as he drove his shortened spear home again. He was dragged to his knees, the wolf almost on top of him, tearing at his shoulder, striving to come at his throat. He drove his chin down on to his breast, and stabbed his spear dagger-wise again and again into its body as they rolled together in the snow. The third wolf was on him now; there was a terrible stricken howling—he did not know whether it was himself or his wolf that howled—a worrying and a snarling and a yelling. There was the taste of blood in his mouth, and a darkness flaring into ragged lights before his eyes . . .

And then the yelling was a different yelling, neither his own nor his wolf's; and the lights were the saffron mare's tails of torches carried by running men—and it was all over. In some unbelievable way it was all over. He was crouching with hanging head in the churned and trampled snow, staring down at the red that blotched and spattered the whiteness. Scarlet on white; Warrior Scarlet; and for a moment he thought hazily that it was the scarlet on the white breast of the swan that had been his first kill. Then his brain cleared somewhat, and he saw that it was blood on snow—hot blood on cold snow, steaming a little in the flaring light of the torches. Old Cu and the she-wolf lay sprawled together, both with their last fight fought, and at a little distance: the third, a young one, snapped and snarled in its death agony, with somebody else's spear through it. But the torch light fell fullest and fiercest on the body of the great grey leader lying outstretched almost against Drem's knee.

There were men all around him; Whitethroat nuzzling into his face, trying to lick all at the same time the torn and streaming wounds in his right arm and breast and shoulder. Someone was supporting him, and he knew that it was Vortrix; and Vortrix's voice was in his ears, lit with a ringing triumph. "He has killed his wolf! See Luga, Urian, a fine Wolf Slaying there has been here! He has killed his wolf!"

"And I think that his wolf has killed him," Urian said.

But Drem only heard them vaguely and a long way off. "Look to Doli," he mumbled. "The ewe too—she—"

"It is well with the ewe." That time it was Hunno's voice. "She needs no looking to."

And suddenly he was aware of the thin crying of a new born lamb; and a moment of swift exultancy leapt in him, not because he had slain the great grey leader, but of all unlikely reasons, because a lamb had come unscathed into the world.

It was the last thing he knew with any clearness for a long time.

INTERESTING FACTS ABOUT THE BRONZE AGE

1. About 2000 B.C. the people of Britain were using implements and utensils made of *stone* so that they were easily conquered by invaders from Europe, who had learned to make *metal weapons*. These invaders had worked with tin and copper and they found that they could make better and stronger weapons by mixing these two minerals to make *bronze*. Pieces of tin and copper were placed in stone bowls and melted in small furnaces. They poured the mixture into moulds or shapes and as it cooled, they hammered it to whatever design they wished.

2. This new metal was more adaptable for their needs than stone. Trees could be cut down, houses could be built more quickly and all sorts of tools and weapons could be fashioned. Axes, spears, daggers, knives and swords gave them a great advantage over their enemies, especially when they had bronze shields with which to protect themselves. Besides these weapons of war, many of which were beautifully designed, bronze ornaments and vessels of fine workmanship were created.

3. The people of the Bronze Age feared the dangers of raiding tribes, but they also had to contend with many hungry, wild animals, which roamed the countryside. Wolves, bears, wild boars and deer were present in large numbers though the larger mammoths and sabre-toothed tigers of the earlier stone age had vanished. Animals like the cow, dog, goat, horse and sheep played an important part in the domestic life of the people.

4. Most villages were situated on high open ground, where cattle grazed and crops were grown. For protection against enemies and wild beasts, these villages were surrounded by high wooden *stockades*. To avoid such dangers, some tribes built *tree-top houses* which could only be entered by means of ladders. Others made *lake-dwellings* which could only be approached by rafts and dug-out canoes. Their food consisted mainly of coarse bannocks, milk, wild fruit, berries, meat and fish; they used earthenware pottery.

5. The people of these villages worked as a team. Men worked with metals, tended flocks, hunted animals or speared fish, while women cooked, wove cloth and ground the grain. Such team-work is noticed in the building of the elaborate *hill-forts*, remains of which can still be seen. They had to depend on one another and usually one man, because of his courage, became leader of the tribe. This chieftain generally wore a special ornament, such as a crown, a necklace or a special kind of feather, and he led them into battle or repelled any enemies, and, in fact, was responsible for the safety of the tribe.

6. Their religion was very simple and primitive. They believed in gods, such as the Sun, Moon and Stars; their priests or *Druids* offered sacrifices, sometimes in human form, to these gods. The Druids were regarded as prophets and were the judges of all tribal quarrels, being honoured by the people as teachers and law-givers. They were also the bards or poets of the tribes, but as writing was unknown, nothing of their songs, laws or wisdom has been preserved.

7. Among the many curious relics of these bygone ages, which can still be seen, are the *menhirs* or huge standing stones set up on end, sometimes with others laid across the top and arranged in circles. *Stonehenge* on Salisbury Plain, probably dates from the Bronze

Age. These circles were probably the centres of religious festivals. The people of the Bronze Age cremated their dead and placed the ashes in urns of beautiful design. The tombs where they placed these urns also contained weapons, helmets, personal ornaments and household vessels belonging to the person who had died. These tombs form a valuable source of our knowledge of the people who once inhabited the British Isles.

8. Trade began with the *barter* system, consisting of an exchange of goods. The metal workers would exchange tools for grain or sheep, and the potter would trade samples of his craft for skins or fish. Gradually the tribes bartered with one another with the products of their own regions. Since tin, which made bronze, was found in Britain, particularly in Cornwall and the isles of Scilly, traders came from other countries to exchange cloth and other luxuries for this valuable metal. Later *salt* and *iron* bars came to be used as forms of currency.

9. There were two areas in Britain where the people of the Bronze Age reached a comparatively high standard of living—the North of England, and Ireland. These people depended largely on *sheep-raising* and *barley-growing*, although they also took part in the flourishing *metal trade* between Ireland and Europe. We can even tell how these ancient men and women were dressed. From what scholars have found in their studies of this far-distant age, it seems that they wore woollen tunics which buttoned down the front.

10. The Bronze Age in Britain came to an end *about* 450 *B.C.*, when the age known as the Iron Age began. This new age marks a great step forward in civilisation, especially in weapons of war, agricultural implements, and general tools. New religions also came to be observed, and, in the sixth century, Christianity was brought by such missionaries as *Saint Columba* to Iona in Scotland and *Saint Augustine* to Kent in England.

QUESTIONS ON THE STORY

1. At what time of year did the incident take place?
2. What was Drem One-arm doing?
3. Of what was he afraid?
4. Why did it not make any difference if the ewe bleated?
5. Whose dog was with him and what was its name?
6. What had happened to the old shepherd?
7. How many wolves were there?
8. What did Drem wish he had been able to do?
9. What did he do when they first approached?
10. What weapons did he have to fight them off?
11. Which wolf attacked Drem?
12. What did the shepherd's dog do?
13. Describe the fight and how it ended.
14. Of what were the torches made?
15. What had been Drem's first kill?
16. What made him remember his first kill at this time?
17. How did the rescuers manage to find Drem?
18. Name three of the rescuers.
19. What sound made Drem very happy and why?
20. What title would Drem receive for killing a wolf unaided?

QUESTIONS ON THE INTERESTING FACTS

1. (a) Why were the people of the Stone Age easily conquered?
   (b) What metals make bronze?
2. (a) Name three advantages of the use of bronze over stone.
   (b) What was created in bronze besides war weapons?

3. (*a*) Name two wild animals of (1) the Stone Age; (2) the Bronze Age.
   (*b*) Name two domestic animals of these early times.
4. (*a*) Why were hill-side villages surrounded by a stockade?
   (*b*) Name two other ways in which houses could be protected.
5. (*a*) How do we know that the villagers worked as a team?
   (*b*) Describe the duties of a chieftain.
6. (*a*) In what Gods did these people believe?
   (*b*) Who were the religious leaders and what were were their duties?
7. (*a*) What relics remain of the Bronze Age?
   (*b*) What was the purpose of the stone circles?
8. (*a*) What is "barter"?
   (*b*) Name two places in Britain where tin was found.
9. Where were the two main centres of Bronze Age civilisation?
10. (*a*) What age succeeded the Bronze Age?
    (*b*) Name two saints who brought Christianity to Britain.

DEVELOPMENT EXERCISES

1. Find on the map of Britain: (*a*) Salisbury Plain; (*b*) Cornwall; (*c*) Kent; (*d*) Scilly Islands; (*e*) Iona.
2. EITHER Describe a day in the life of a Bronze Age villager.
   OR Write a sentence on each of the following: (*a*) Stone Age; (*b*) Bronze Age; (*c*) Iron Age; (*d*) Elizabethan Age; (*e*) Atomic Age.
3. The young of a ewe is a lamb. Name the young of the following: (*a*) boar; (*b*) elephant; (*c*) goat; (*d*) horse; (*e*) wolf.

4. Whitethroat was the name given to the dog. With what animals do you associate the following names. (*a*) Bambi; (*b*) Bruin; (*c*) Dobbin; (*d*) Jumbo; (*e*) Leo?

5. A shepherd looks after sheep. What name is given to the following people?
   (*a*) One who looks after animals on an estate.
   (*b*) One who looks after a factory at night.
   (*c*) One who looks after a house.
   (*d*) One who looks after pigs.
   (*e*) One who looks after a school.

6. "Saffron" is a yellowish-red colour. In what main colours would you describe (*a*) beige; (*b*) dun; (*c*) indigo; (*d*) lilac; (*e*) mauve?

7. A tribal chief is recognised by the eagle's feathers he wears. How would you recognise (*a*) a king; (*b*) a mayor; (*c*) a clergyman; (*d*) a sergeant; (*e*) a nurse?

8. Stonehenge is an ancient Druid monument. Where are the following, (*a*) the Colosseum; (*b*) Grant's Tomb; (*c*) The Leaning Tower; (*d*) The Pyramids; (*e*) The Taj-Mahal?

THE STORY OF OIL

For thousands of years, the practical usefulness of petroleum or "rock oil" was realised and exploited, though not in the manner in which we use it to-day. The ancient Chinese, for example, used oil for heating and lighting; the Red Indians applied it to cure war wounds; caravans of asses carried it from the shores of the Caspian Sea all over Persia for use in lamps, and the pioneers in their covered wagons used it as axle grease during their trek across America.

The value of oil is now appreciated all over the world. The chief oil-fields are in the United States of America, Canada, Mexico, South America, Soviet Russia, Rumania, Arabia, Egypt, Iran, Iraq, Indonesia, Nigeria, the Sahara Desert and Great Britain, and this product forms a great source of wealth.

HOW was oil created? Far back in prehistoric times, millions of animals and plants lived in shallow seas. When they died, they sank to the sea-bed, where they decayed and were soon covered with mud. In time, these fossils became buried deeper and deeper, and were squeezed tighter and tighter, until they oozed tiny drops of oil. From these countless drops are formed the great oilfields of to-day. Contrary to what is thought by most people, oil does not exist in vast subterranean pools. A typical oilfield consists of a cap of hard solid rock, under which are found petroleum gases, liquid oil and

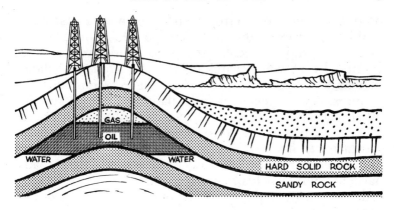

water, all held in a layer of sandy rock, rather like water in a sponge. As the years pass, the oil travels along the layer or stratum, so that, where oil-fields were once below the sea, many may now be far inland or even beneath mountains. Some oil deposits may be only a few hundred feet under the surface while others are over four miles beneath the earth's crust.

In Scotland, around 1850, Dr. James Young extracted oily substances from certain types of coal and shale, and thus discovered paraffin. In England, notably in Nottinghamshire, machines have been installed called "yes-nodders"; they derive this odd name from the fact that they resemble someone nodding his head. The oil is pumped to the surface and led away by underground pipes to storage tanks.

The first well was struck in Pennsylvania by Colonel Edwin Drake in 1859, at a depth of 69 feet. His success started an oil "boom", and within a year, over half a million barrels of oil had been produced in this area. Later, oil was discovered in Colorado and in many other parts of the United States. In those early days, the valuable part of the oil was the paraffin, which was heated in simple pot stills, while most of the other products, including petrol, were thrown away as waste.

When, however, the great uses to which oil could be put were known, geologists, who study rocks, were continually at work searching for oil, from the coldest regions to the tropics, in deserts, jungles, mountains and swamps. After the geologists had made their reports, other scientists went out with very sensitive instruments to test any place likely to contain oil. If their tests were satisfactory, new oil wells were drilled. Oil is often discovered in out-of-the-way places, so that roads, harbours and airfields may have sometimes to be built in order to bring equipment, labour, housing, food and water supplies to the site.

An oilfield can be found not only below the earth's surface but also below the sea. When this occurs a drilling platform is set up on piers which have their foundations on the sea-bed.

To reach the oil or where they think oil will be found, engineers bore down through the earth, sometimes for as much as a mile or more. This is done by erecting a derrick or framework structure above the place to be bored, and the drilling is done by means of a rotating table driven by an engine. This rotating table turns the boring tool round and round, causing it to go deeper and deeper. The drill is hollow and as the rock is ground away, water is pumped down which turns the ground rock into mud, and this mud is in turn washed to the surface. Millions of gallons of oil may be released when the bore reaches oil-bearing rock, so to prevent a blow-out or "gusher", the flow is capped and the derrick and drilling gear removed. In their place a "Christmas tree" contraption of pipes, valves and taps is fixed, thus bringing the output of oil under complete control.

When large quantities of liquid require to be moved overland, the best way of doing it is by pipeline. The longest pipe lines for transporting oil are to be found in the Middle East, where they stretch from the Persian Gulf to the Mediterranean Sea, a distance of over a thousand miles. Every fifty miles along the line are pumping stations, from which maintenance men keep a watchful eye on the line for leaks or faults.

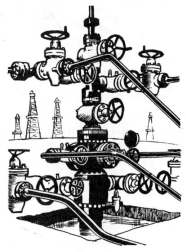

Tankers carry a great deal of oil to all countries and more than a quarter of the merchant ship tonnage in the world, is composed of oil-tankers. These vessels have their engines and funnels at the stern and practically all the rest of the ship consists of oil-storage tanks. For safety's sake, the fore and aft parts of the tanker are separated by a three foot wide watertight barrier called a coffer dam.

There are various stages in purifying the oil as it comes from the ground. The crude oil is heated in a refinery tower until it gives off a gas which, when it cools, becomes liquid again. This is petrol or motor spirit. When it is heated a little more, the crude oil gives off

another vapour which becomes diesel oil when cooled. Further heating and further cooling gives "kerosene" or paraffin for use in lamps and heaters: next follow lubricating oils of different grades, and finally, the paraffin wax that is used in making candles.

Besides these various oils, the refineries also provide other very useful by-products, such as tar and the chemicals which the farmer puts on his fields to help his crops grow. Petroleum is used to a great extent in the manufacture of plastic and polythene articles, as well as in the making of cleaning detergents for the housewife.

Oil in some form or another is used in all parts of the world. The factory needs its fuel oil and lubricating oil to drive its machinery, buses and lorries require heavy motor spirit, cars use petrol, the airport has its aviation spirit, the farmer needs tractor fuel, railways and ships use diesel oil, and even the road-maker's bitumen comes from the refinery. Over half the power in the world comes from oil and as the years pass, its value is becoming even greater.

DEVELOPMENT EXERCISES

1. On the map of the world point out the following oil-bearing countries: (*a*) U.S.A.; (*b*) Egypt; (*c*) Soviet Russia; (*d*) Iran; (*e*) Canada; (*f*) Rumania; (*g*) South America; (*h*) Indonesia; (*i*) Mexico.
2. In what way was rock-oil first used by (*a*) Red Indians; (*b*) Chinese; (*c*) the American Pioneers?
3. Describe briefly the digging of an oil-well.
4. (*a*) Who struck the first oil-well?
   (*b*) In the early days, what part of the oil was used and what was run to waste?
5. (*a*) How do drillers control the flow of oil?
   (*b*) Describe how they bore for oil beneath the sea.
6. What is meant by (*a*) a yes-nodder; (*b*) a derrick; (*c*) a coffer dam?
7. Describe how oil is carried overland.
8. In what ways does a tanker differ from a cargo vessel?
9. For what are the following used: (*a*) olive oil; (*b*) cod liver oil; (*c*) castor oil; (*d*) ground-nut oil; (*e*) palm oil?
10. A tanker is used to carry oil. What do the following vessels carry: (*a*) a tramp; (*b*) a trawler; (*c*) a liner; (*d*) a carrier; (*e*) a dredger?

THE CATTLE STAMPEDE

Sir Michael Bruce spent an adventurous life in many parts of the world and in his autobiography "Tramp Royal", he tells of this exciting incident which occurred in South America.—[ABRIDGED.]

I FINALLY accepted a job as livestock manager to the Armour Meat Company at Frigerifico, near São Paulo. The Company wanted a man who could ride, who knew something about cattle and could talk Portuguese. I seemed to fit the bill, and I accepted with alacrity.

Armour's, the great meat canners and refrigerators, bring the cattle in from the Brazilian Highlands: ponderous beasts of mixed breeds, as wild as could be expected, animals which had roamed the Matto Grosso and never seen a human until the annual round-up when the up-country cattlemen collect them in their hundreds and drive them to the railway stations. Some of the drives are 500 miles long and take up to four months. On their way to the paddocks the cattle must never be hurried. They must feed as they trek for their weight must be kept up.

Each paddock is 5,000 acres large and is shaped like a vast segment of orange. The land is covered with rich, coarse grass. Here and there are occasional ravines of sore red earth and tropical plants and reddish trees, their trunks polished bright by the rubbing of a million beasts.

We went out, riding to the extreme end of the paddock about fifteen miles from the gates. There were eight of us: two Britons, a joyous Southern American called Carolina, who sang all the time, and five peons. At the far end of the paddock we sat around the fire or lay rolled in our blankets. Carolina, who had all the charm, courtesy, courage and kindliness that distinguishes the Southerner from his more brash Northern neighbour, sang softly. The smoke from the fire kept away the mosquitoes but not the cattle-ticks, big insects which attacked us mercilessly.

The night was desperately cold and black. Our ponies were restless, the fire spluttered. At last we slept, to awaken in a heavy mist of damp, pearly dew. It rested on everything; on blankets, ponies, boots, saddles and men. The whole landscape was lost in the dense whiteness.

It was three o'clock. The cook, a Brazilian with a squint—he could say "Go to blazes" in fourteen languages —was making coffee. We rolled out of our blankets and

the cook swam out of the mist with the steaming cups. We gulped the hot liquid, unhobbled our horses—they were small animals with big shoulders and as quick on their feet as lightning. Then we faced the white mist.

We parted. The eight men formed a line along the top end of the paddock and then, at a shout, we rode slowly into the mist. It was so thick it seemed to brush against us like a gigantic clammy blanket. I could not see the man on my left but I could hear Carolina singing cheerfully somewhere on my right. There was nothing to tell us if a beast was between us except the wonderful instinct of our horses, which would swerve out towards something that became a dark lump on the ground and rose with a snort to stagger off ahead of us.

Gradually there was a glow in the white pall, as if the sun was trying to break through. The cattle heard our thumping hooves. Their black shapes appeared mistily, like hummocks, but they moved off, in front of us, in the direction of the paddock gates. I saw before me one, two, three vague shapes, then, on my left, there was a shout: "Look out!" A steer had turned and tried to break back, to run between us. A peon whirled past, a

steer almost at his quarter. The mists seemed to curdle around them and a fifteen feet long whip lash, split the mists like a knife through icing. You could see the split where the lash had passed.

The peon overtook the steer. It turned. Its great hooves beat the earth but in a moment it became merged in the great mass of moving shapes in front of us.

I was acting as herd leader, which meant that it was my turn to ride ahead of the herd to check them at the latch-post. I rode down into the mist. I could hear Carolina singing. The vague forms of the cattle kept moving in the silver-white haze. There was uneasiness in the air. We felt that something had worried the cattle. Perhaps a puma had moved across the land, or the wind was bringing the smell of death from the slaughter-house, but the horse-boys were kept constantly on the move checking the break-backs.

I pushed my way through the herd for the gates. There was no doubt that they were restless. They were half-running before I was through them and the flank riders were cracking their whips and shouting in their attempts to hold them.

I got through the herd safely and then, a few yards ahead of them, my pony slipped and fell. It rolled over, pinning my leg under the saddle. I remember the awful distortion of sky, of rushing earth, the thud as I hit the ground and then the sight of hundreds of beasts lumbering towards me. Something had frightened them—afterwards I learned that it was a dog that had run across the paddock to join the round-up—and they were running now. I struggled to raise myself but could not. I flung myself back to the ground. There was no escape. The pony would not move. I pulled my Winchester from its sheath on the saddle bucket and wriggled close in against the body of the pony. I saw the herd a yard or two away, and emptied my rifle at them. Then I closed my eyes. There was nothing to do now but to wait for death.

I buried my face in the warm-smelling hide of the pony. I crept so close that I felt his muscles move against me. He struggled for a moment and my face became damp from the sweat on his coat. Suddenly he rose a fraction and quivered; then fell back on me.

We had rolled into a depression. Just as I fell back I opened my eyes and saw first one and then another steer stumble. I felt them hit the pony and felt the pony's body weigh heavily down on me. Then the herd thundered over us. I seemed to be hammered into the earth. I was almost stifled by the sweating, heavy bodies above me. I seemed to be surrounded, smothered. Then my senses left me.

When I came round they were bathing my forehead and Carolina was saying, over and over again; "A miracle! A miracle!" I tried to move but every bone and muscle was crushed and bruised. I felt them lift me on to the chuck wagon and then lost consciousness once more.

A day or two later Carolina came to see me in the Armour Company's private hospital. He told me I had fallen into a hole with the pony on top, just where the paddock narrowed. The whole herd seemed to have passed right over me. My pony was dead but its body, and the bodies of two steers which I had either hit with my bullets or which had tripped and fallen, had acted as a carpet that saved my life.

I lay in the Company's hospital for six weeks before I could walk again and then, as I had been warned that I would have to take life quietly for a while, I went to convalesce with a Brazilian friend who had a ranch up-country in São Paulo.

INTERESTING FACTS ABOUT SOUTH AMERICA

1. Although it has an area nearly twice that of Europe, South America has a population only twice that of the British Isles. Most of South America lies within the tropical zone, so that the lowlands are generally very hot. The river *Amazon*, 3,500 miles long, flows along the Equator to the Atlantic Ocean. South America is joined to the northern part of the continent by the isthmus of Panama. Its southernmost point is Cape Horn which used to be dreaded by sailors who had to make the journey from the Atlantic to the Pacific Ocean before the *Panama Canal* was constructed.

2. Down the west coast like a backbone stretch the long, high mountain ranges of the *Andes*, once the home of the Incas. The first inhabitants of South America were Indians, and though the natives in the lowlands were backward and remained simple hunters, the *Incas* or "Children of the Sun" reached a highly civilised state. They were highly skilled in making wonderful gold and jewelled ornaments and pottery and they lived

in great cities, the ruins of which can still be seen.

3. During the 16th century, the *Spanish* and *Portuguese* conquerors robbed the people of their gold and silver treasures. They did nothing to develop the country so that gradually the people broke away from their distant European rulers. Except for the small colonies of British, Dutch and French Guiana, South America is divided into ten republics, in nine of which a kind of Spanish is spoken, while in one, Brazil, they retain the customs and language of Portugal.

4. The low lying lands of South America can be divided into four sections: (*a*) In the north, stretches the *savanna*, a vast series of treeless plains known as the "*llanos*"; (*b*) The hot, steaming basin of the Amazon is covered with dense tropical forests called the *selvas*; (*c*) Further south of the wooded areas formed by the plateau of the Matto Grosso (the Great Woods) and El Gran Chaco (the Great Hunting Ground) lie the *pampas* lands famous for cattle rearing; (*d*) Towards the tip of South America, the lowlands become the barren plains and stony deserts of Patagonia.

5. The *gaucho* is a cattleman somewhat similar to a cowboy, only much more gaily clothed. He wears a sombrero of black felt, a highly coloured neckerchief and a white shirt, adorned with lace, under a short, black silk embroidered jacket. He has a broad ornamented belt, from which protrudes a silver-hilted knife and he is generally mounted on a stocky pinto pony. The gauchos receive their name from their being lonely men, often without family, the word coming from a Spanish word meaning, "a motherless calf". Farm labourers on the "estancias" or ranches are called *peons*.

6. The *bolas* is a kind of lasso used for catching cattle. It consists of three round balls of lead or pebbles, encased in raw leather and roped together. It is whirled round and round over the gaucho's head and thrown at the animal's legs, to trip it up so that it can be easily captured. The bolas is sometimes called the "Three Marys" (Tres Marias). *Nazarenes* are large silver spurs worn by gauchos and are so-called because they were the type of spurs traditionally worn by the first Christian conquerors. A *poncho* is a long piece of cloth, made from a fine mixture of wool and cotton, which is equivalent in shape and purpose to the Scottish plaid.

7. In early times gold coins, about the size of a crown piece, were minted at Cuzco in Bolivia, and circulated throughout the country; these were called "*Bolivianos*". From the beginning of this century each country in South America made its own coins; Argentine used pesos and centavos while Brazil had reis and milreis. In recent years efforts have been made to establish a common currency throughout the whole of South America.

8. There are many interesting plants and trees in South America. Ebony, rosewood and mahogany are plentiful, as are rubber and coconut trees. The *quebracho*, meaning "break-axe" is a hard-wood tree, the bark of which is used in tanning, while from the dried powdered bark of the *cinchona* tree, quinine is prepared. Another useful medical preparation, cocaine, is obtained from the leaves of the *coca* tree. Near the coast, the *cacao* plant produces the seeds from which cocoa and chocolate are manufactured, while on the slopes there are large coffee plantations. Paraguay tea or *mate* is obtained from a tree of the holly family; it is a kind of drug which drives away tiredness of mind and body. Sugar-cane and tobacco are also extensively grown. *Alfalfa* is a clover-like plant which is used as fodder.

9. Herds of *llamas* are bred on the foothills of the Andes and these are used as beasts of burden, while the vicuna and alpaca, which are also smaller members of the camel family, are bred for their long, fine wool.

The forests abound in wild beasts, such as the tapir, puma, jaguar and monkey, but even more typical of the country are *sloths*, *ant-eaters* and *armadillos*. Myriads of brilliantly coloured humming-birds, macaws and parrots inhabit the tropical forests. The *condor* of the Andes is a type of eagle and is the best known bird of prey.

10. *Buenos Aires*, the capital of Argentine, is the largest city in the southern hemisphere, containing over $4\frac{1}{2}$ million people. It has many beautiful buildings, fine open squares and public parks. It is the starting point for the railways which connect the pampas lands with the sea. *Rio de Janeiro*, the former capital of Brazil, has a beautiful harbour and is a most colourful seaport. It has a wonderful climate, being just north of the Tropic of Capricorn; Rio has magnificent hotels and beaches, which make it a popular holiday resort. The Brazilians have built a new inland capital called *Brasilia*, which is the first large city in the world entirely planned in the most modern style of architecture. The centre of the Brazilian government is now situated there. Other large cities in South America are Montevideo, Valparaiso, Lima, Quito and Georgetown.

QUESTIONS ON THE STORY

1. Where did the story take place?
2. Who is telling the story?
3. Why was he most suited to this job?
4. How often were the cattle rounded up and why were they so wild?
5. Why was it important that the cattle should not be hurried?
6. How many were in the herding party and who were they?
7. What was the difference between a North American and a South American?
8. What was remarkable about (a) the Brazilian cook; (b) Carolina?
9. Describe the ponies used in the round-up.
10. At what time of day and in what kind of weather did the round-up take place?

11. What happened when a steer broke back from the herd?
12. What is meant by being a "herd-leader"?
13. What reasons did the drovers give for the uneasiness in the herd?
14. Why was the herd-leader sure that the cattle had been disturbed?
15. What happened when he got through the herd?
16. Why could he not break loose from the pony?
17. Where did the herd-leader carry his rifle?
18. Why did he fire the shots at the oncoming cattle?
19. How did he manage to escape certain death?
20. What was the true explanation of the cause of the stampede?

QUESTIONS ON THE INTERESTING FACTS

1. (a) Why is South America regarded as "a land of opportunity"?
   (b) What is the quickest sea route from New York to Valparaiso?
2. (a) What is the name of the range of mountains that stretches the length of South America?
   (b) Tell what you know of the Incas.
3. (a) Name the conquerors of South America.
   (b) How many colonies are there in South America and name the British one?
4. (a) What is savanna?
   (b) Give another name for the tropical forests of the Amazon.
   (c) For what are the pampas used?
5. Describe a gaucho. How does he differ from a cowboy?
6. (a) Give another name for the bolas. What is its purpose?

    (*b*) What are Nazarenes?

    (*c*) With what Scottish garment would you compare a poncho?

7. (*a*) What was the size of a Boliviano and of what metal was it made?

    (*b*) Name any form of currency in South America.

8. Name (*a*) three beverages; (*b*) two medical products and the trees or plants from which they are obtained.

9. (*a*) Give the names of three typical animals in South America.

    (*b*) What is the best-known bird of prey?

10. (*a*) Name the largest town in the Southern hemisphere.

    (*b*) Name the new capital of Brazil.

    (*c*) Name three more towns in South America.

DEVELOPMENT EXERCISES

1. Point out on the map of South America. (*a*) The Andes; (*b*) Cape Horn; (*c*) Matto Grosso; (*d*) São Paulo; (*e*) Tropic of Capricorn.

2. EITHER (*a*) Point out the differences between herding cattle in this country and herding cattle in South America.

    OR   (*b*) Write a short autobiography of a penny or an old shoe.

3. An autobiography is the life story of the person who is writing it. What is the name given to a story that tells (*a*) another person's life story; (*b*) a person's day to day experiences; (*e*) a person's reminiscences?

4. (1) Autobiography is derived from Greek autos = self; bios = life; graphein = to write. Find out the meanings and derivations of (*a*) autograph, automatic, automobile, autonomy. (*b*) calligraphy, geography, photography, telegraphy.

5. A collection or group of cattle is called a herd. Name a collection or group of (*a*) lions; (*b*) monkeys; (*c*) pups; (*d*) sheep; (*e*) wolves.

6. A Winchester is an American rifle. With what country or race do you associate the following weapons: (*a*) assegai; (*b*) bolas; (*c*) boomerang; (*d*) claymore; (*e*) harpoon?

7. "Perhaps a puma had moved across the land." The puma is a member of the wild-cat family from South America. Name five other wild cats and the country with which each is associated.

8. "The paddock was like a vast segment of orange." When we compare two things and say one is "like" the other, we are using a figure of speech called a *simile*. Complete the following similes:—
(*a*) The runner started like an——from a bow.
(*b*) The coward was trembling like a——.
(*c*) Her face was as——as a sheet.
(*d*) When he won the prize it was like a——from the blue.
(*e*) He considered his good fortune as——from heaven.

9. The people of Argentine use pesos and centavos. What country uses each of the following units of currency: (*a*) dollar; (*b*) franc; (*c*) lira; (*d*) rouble; (*e*) yen?

10. The savanna is the treeless flat land of South America. With what country do you associate the following large stretches of land: (*a*) deccan; (*b*) meseta; (*c*) prairie; (*d*) steppes; (*e*) veld?

THE FORTUNE TELLER

Mr Rochester, one of the main characters in Charlotte Bronte's famous novel "Jane Eyre", stoops to a little deception in order to find out the truth about certain things. The story is told by Jane Eyre, who is a governess at the home of the wealthy Mr. Rochester.

THE library looked quiet enough as I entered it, and the witch—if she really were such—was seated in an armchair by the fire. She had a loose red garment wrapped around her and a wide hat tied down with a handkerchief under her chin. She seemed to be reading from a little black book, and murmured the words to herself, as most old women do, while she read.

The woman shut her book and her eyes met mine with a bold and direct gaze though her hat partly shaded her face.

"Well, and you want your fortune told?" she said in a voice as rough as her appearance.

"I don't care about it; but I ought to warn you, I shall not believe you."

"It's the sort of answer I expected from you. I heard it in your step as you came in."

"Did you? You've a quick ear."

"I have; and a quick eye and a quick brain. I need them; especially when I've people like you to deal with: Why don't you tremble?"

"I'm not cold."

"Why don't you turn pale?"

"I am not sick."

"Why don't you consult me about your future?"

"I am not silly."

The old woman gave a high thin-sounding laugh, and lighting a short black pipe, began to smoke. After several minutes, she raised her bent body, took the pipe from her lips, and said :

"You are cold; you are sick; and you are silly."

"Prove it," I returned.

"You are cold, because you are alone. Nothing strikes the fire from you that is in you. You are sick, because the best of feelings, the highest and sweetest given to man, keeps away from you. You are silly, because however much you suffer, you will make no sign to it to approach, nor will you stir one step to meet it where it waits you."

"You might say that to almost anyone living in my circumstances."

"There is scarcely anyone living in just your circumstances. If you knew it, you are peculiarly situated: very near happiness; yes, within reach of it; only a movement is needed to combine the materials".

"I don't understand mysteries."

"If you wish me to speak more plainly, show me your hand."

"And I must cross it with silver, I suppose"

"Of course."

I gave her a shilling. She put it in an old stocking, tied it up and approached her face to my hand.

"It is too fine," she said. "I cannot read it. Besides fate is not written in a hand. It is in the face. Kneel and lift up your head."

As I obeyed, she stirred the fire so that a flicker of light broke from the disturbed coal and fell full upon me.

"I wonder what thoughts are busy in your heart

during all the hours you sit among the fine people yonder," she said, when she had examined me a while.

"I feel tired often, sleepy sometimes, but seldom sad."

"Then you have some secret hope to support you and please you with whispers of the future?"

"Not I. The most I hope is to save enough money to set up a little school of my own some day."

"A poor food for the spirit to exist on: and sitting in that window-seat (you see I know your habits) . . ."

"You have learnt them from the servants."

"Ah! You think yourself sharp. Well, to tell the truth. I am acquainted with one of them, Mrs. Poole . . ."

I started to my feet.

"You are . . . are you?" I thought: "there is something queer about this."

"Don't be alarmed," continued the strange creature. "You can trust Mrs. Poole, she can keep a secret. But as I was saying: sitting in that window-seat, do you think of nothing but your future school? Is there not one face that you study? Or maybe two?"

"I like to study all the faces."

"But when a lady, young and beautiful and of high rank, sits and smiles in the eyes of a gentleman whom you . . ."

"Whom what?"

"Whom you know . . . and perhaps think well of him."

"I don't know the gentlemen here. I have scarcely spoken a word to any of them."

"Will you say that of the master of the house?"

"He is not at home."

"And because he is away from here for a few hours, do you then deny his acquaintance?"

"No, but I do not see what Mr. Rochester has to do with the subject."

"I was talking of ladies smiling into the eyes of gentlemen."

"Mr. Rochester has a right to enjoy the society of his guests."

"Yes, Mr. Rochester has sat for hours, his ear towards those charming lips, looking grateful for the entertainment given him."

"Grateful! I cannot remember observing gratitude in his face."

"Observing! You have watched him closely then. What do you observe, if not gratitude? You have seen love, have you not? . . . and, looking into the future, you have seen him married and his bride happy?"

"Not exactly. Your witch's skill is at fault sometimes."

"What in the world have you seen, then?"

"Never mind: I came here to inquire, not to confess. Is it known that Mr. Rochester is to be married?"

"Yes, and to the beautiful Miss Ingram. He must love such a fair lady and probably she loves him, or at least his purse. Yet I told her something about the Rochester property half an hour ago, that made her look rather anxious."

"But you have told me nothing of my own fortune."

"Yours is as yet doubtful; kneel again on the rug."

"Don't keep me long for the fire burns me."

"The flame flickers in the eye: the eye shines like dew; it looks soft and full of feeling; it smiles at my words: it is open to influence. When it ceases to smile it is sad: it shows heaviness of spirit resulting from loneliness. The eye is favourable.

"As to the mouth, it delights at times in laughter. It is a mouth that requires affection. That too is favourable.

"I can see no enemy but in the forehead, and that forehead seems to say: 'I can live alone, if self-respect and circumstances require me to do so.'

"Well said, forehead; your declaration shall be respected. I have formed my plans and my harvest must be smiles not tears. But I have said enough. Rise, Miss Eyre, leave me, the play is over."

Where was I? Did I wake or sleep? The old woman's voice had changed: it was now as familiar to me as my own face in a glass. I got up but did not go. The witch again made a sign to me to depart. The fire shone on her arm: it was round, not withered: a broad ring flashed on the little finger: I had seen it many times before.

"Well, Jane, do you know me?" asked the familiar voice.

"Only take off these red rags sir, and then . . ."

"But the string is in a knot . . . help me."

"Break it, sir."

"There, then . . ." And Mr. Rochester stepped out of his borrowed garments.

"Now, sir, what a strange idea!"

"But well carried out, eh? Don't you think so?"

"With the ladies you must have managed well."

"But not with you?"

"You did not act the character of a witch with me."

"What character did I act? My own?"

"No, I believe you have been trying to make me speak too freely : you have been talking nonsense to make me talk nonsense. It is scarcely fair, sir."

"Do you forgive me, Jane?"

"I cannot tell till I have thought about it. If, on reflection, I find I have said nothing very foolish, I shall try to forgive you but it was not right."

"Oh, you have been very correct—very careful, very sensible."

I reflected, and thought, on the whole, I had. It was a comfort: but, indeed, I had been suspicious almost from the beginning of the interview. I knew that fortune-tellers did not express themselves like this seeming old woman. My mind, however, had been full of Grace Poole but I had never thought of Mr. Rochester.

INTERESTING FACTS ABOUT MAGIC
AND SUPERSTITION

1. From earliest times, people believed in *magic*. If something occurred for which there seemed no reasonable or natural explanation then it was regarded as super-natural. Early forms of magic were spread and kept alive among savages, by tribal leaders, by the *medicine men* of the Red Indians and by the *witch doctors* of Africa and elsewhere. They painted themselves elaborately and were frighteningly attired, thus causing the primitive people to hold them in great awe. By tricks and devices, they overcame evil spirits, brought rain, ensured good crops or gained victories. Witch-doctors were usually skilled in reading weather signs and in effecting simple cures, but often they used this knowledge to their own personal advantage.

2. Among the ancient civilised races, destiny was controlled by the *gods*, who were responsible for the good or bad fortune which attended certain aspects of life. The *Romans* had many gods and goddesses, like Ceres, the goddess of harvest and Mars, the god of war. The *Greeks* also believed in more than one god, like Zeus, the supreme god and Aphrodite, goddess of love. The *Norse* gods, such as Thor the god of thunder, were worshipped by the people of northern Europe.

3. Closely linked with the performance of magic were *wizards* and *witches*. The former, according to traditional

stories, had magic wands which, when waved in a certain manner, would make people and things disappear. The latter were pictured as old hags with tall, conical hats, who flew from place to place on a broomstick. They usually frequented dark, lonely places and stirred a cauldron which contained a horrible and foul-smelling brew, from which they made evil potions. In England and Scotland all witchcraft Acts of Parliament were repealed in 1736, in Ireland not until 1821. At one time anyone possessing such wicked powers was taken and burned at the stake.
Shakespeare's "Macbeth" and Burns' "Tam O'Shanter" give famous accounts of the behaviour of witches.

4. Certain places and buildings are said to be haunted by *ghosts*. Stories are invented by imaginative people to explain mysterious noises and occurrences and, in order to make the stories sound more convincing, they introduced the idea of spirits of dead people as wraiths, "spooks" or ghosts. Often the noises were weird sounds caused by the wind or by creaking doors and, in deserted buildings, the presence of bats flying through the darkness gave the impression of ghosts flitting around the place.

5. There are a great many actions which superstitious people connect with *ill-omen*. Breaking a mirror is reckoned to bring seven years of bad luck to the culprit, while walking under a ladder, or dropping a glove, are also interpreted as foretelling bad times. If thirteen sit at a table or a person spills salt, it is said that bad luck is imminent, though the spell may be broken, as in the

last instance, when a pinch of salt thrown over the left
shoulder, restores things to normal.

6. It has always been believed that besides counter-
acting ill-fortune, mascots and charms can bring the
bearer *good luck*. In ancient times, bells were used to
drive away demons, amulets were worn to ward off
the evil eye and a sprig of rowan (mountain ash) kept
away evil spirits. Some of these superstitions have been
kept up through the centuries and often gave the wearer
of charms a feeling of comfort. A horse-shoe, a rabbit's
foot, white heather or a four-leaf clover are a few of the
symbols of good luck, but as luck is a very fickle thing,
no one should rely on the power of these charms to
bring good fortune.

7. People everywhere are curious about the future,
wanting to know whether they are likely to succeed in
life or what is going to happen in their business or
love affairs. Anyone therefore who claims to be able
to foretell the future is regarded as an extraordinary
person. *Soothsayers, oracles* and *diviners* used to be asked
by rulers if they would be successful in war and even
today, Chinese business men consult the so-called wise
prophets before making a big business deal. The most
famous temple of prophecy in the ancient past was the
Oracle of Delphi in Greece, where, for many centuries,
prophetesses spoke as the voice of the god Apollo about
future happenings. Often the answer to the question had
two meanings, so that whatever happened the prophecy
could be said to have come true.

8. At fairs and carnivals, women of the Romany race, that is the wandering *gypsies*, claim, for a sum of money, to foretell the future by gazing into a *crystal* ball. The reflections created in this glass ball are supposed to make shapes whereby the gypsy conjures up the future. By studying bumps on the head or reading the palm of the hand, all kinds of good and bad fortune seem to be revealed to them. In Scotland, the *"spae-wife"* reads the leaves in a tea-cup or tells what is about to happen from looking at playing cards.

9. *"Marry in May and repent for aye"* is one of the old superstitious tags attached to a wedding in a month that was regarded by the Romans as unlucky. *"Something old something new, something borrowed and something blue,"* brings luck to the bride, and if a *black cat* crosses their path on the way out of church, an assured life of good fortune awaits the happy couple. Besides being a symbol of good luck, the black cat was regarded by the Egyptians as an object of worship. The reason may have been that in a country, which had huge grain stores to prevent famine, the cat was invaluable for destroying rats. Seafaring men are notoriously superstitious; ships rarely sail on *Friday the thirteenth* and it brings ill-luck to harm or kill sea-birds, whereas if porpoises follow a ship, it is interpreted as a token of a successful voyage.

10. Many fortune-tellers use the stars and the *signs of the Zodiac* as their means of forecasting. That the

CAPRICORN   AQUARIUS   PISCES

ARIES   TAURUS   GEMINI

CANCER   LEO   VIRGO

LIBRA   SCORPIO   SAGITTARIUS

movements of stars are supposed to have a close connection with the fortunes of people is an old pagan idea. In this way guesses are hazarded as to the future of nations and individuals by observing the stars. No person, however wise or clever, can be certain of the future and fortune-tellers have not the powers which foolish people believe them to possess. Magic and superstition are relics of fear and ignorance and, when taken seriously, should be discouraged. It is a great pity that many newspapers and periodicals still publish such nonsense as, "What the stars foretell" or "The stars and you", without heading such material as "fiction" or "for amusement only".

QUESTIONS ON THE STORY

1. Who is telling the story?
2. Describe how the fortune-teller was dressed.
3. What did the witch ask her to do before she attempted to read her hand?
4. What was Jane's ambition?
5. Who was the master of the house and where was he supposed to be?
6. To whom was he to be married?
7. In what way did the fortune teller test the love of the bride-to-be?
8. Why do you think the marriage will not take place?
9. What did Mr. Rochester learn by his deception?
10. Do you think the deception was fair?

QUESTIONS ON THE INTERESTING FACTS

1. (*a*) Name two types of primitive magicians.
   (*b*) What did they claim to be able to do?

2. Name three ancient gods or goddesses and tell what they controlled.

3. (*a*) What fate awaited anyone who claimed to be a witch?
   (*b*) Name two works of literature dealing with the supernatural.

4. (*a*) What people do ghosts usually represent?
   (*b*) What is likely to give the impression of a ghost in an empty building?

5. (*a*) Name three actions that are supposed to bring bad luck.
   (*b*) What breaks the spell if salt is spilt?

6. (*a*) For what were charms used in ancient times?
   (*b*) Name three symbols of good luck that are worn.

7. (*a*) Where was the most famous oracle?
   (*b*) Why did it seem that their prophecies came true?

8. (*a*) What race of people tell fortunes for money?
   (*b*) Why is a crystal ball used?
   (*c*) What is a "spae-wife"?

9. (*a*) What month did the Romans regard as unlucky?
   (*b*) What would bring good luck to a couple that were going to be married?
   (*c*) What superstition is said to ensure success for a ship?

10. (*a*) To what are birthdays supposed to be related?
    (*b*) In what way do newspapers encourage superstitions?

DEVELOPMENT EXERCISES

1. A witch is concerned with magic. In what way are the following connected with magic or superstition (a) a goblin; (b) a genie; (c) a fairy; (d) an elf; (e) a nymph?

2. EITHER (a) Give a short account of a time when you dressed in fancy clothes.
   OR (b) Tell a short story of a night in a haunted house.

3. Make a list of the things which bring (a) good luck; (b) bad luck.

4. The feminine of wizard is witch. What is the feminine of (a) bachelor; (b) duke; (c) emperor; (d) tutor; (e) widower?

5. Gypsies are of the wandering Romany race. To what country do each of the following people belong (a) Cossacks; (b) Eskimos; (c) Dutch; (d) Kaffirs; (e) Jews?

6. Name some of the differences between a conjuror and a magician.

7. Write a short note on each of the following: (a) wishing-well; (b) well-wisher; (c) wishbone; (d) wishy-washy; (e) wishful thinking.

8. Some lucky mascots are associated with places. With what parts of the British Isles are the following lucky charms connected: (a) four-leafed shamrock; (b) white heather; (c) cat without a tail; (d) pixie; (e) leprechaun?

9. The story you have just read is mainly in the form of a dialogue, that is a conversation between two people. Find out what the following mean: (a) catalogue; (b) decalogue; (c) epilogue; (d) monologue; (e) prologue.

THE CAVALIER'S ESCAPE

Trample! trample! went the roan,
Trap! trap! went the grey;
But pad! *pad*! PAD! like a thing that was mad,
My chestnut broke away.
It was just five miles from Salisbury town
And but one hour to day.

Thud! thud! came on the heavy roan,
Rap! rap! the mettled grey;
But my chestnut mare was of blood so rare
That she showed them all the way.
Spur on! spur on!—I doffed my hat,
And wished them all good-day.

They splashed through miry rut and pool—
Splintered through fence and rail;
But chestnut Kate switched over the gate—
I saw them droop and tail:
To Salisbury town—but a mile of down,
Over this brook and rail.

Trap! trap! I heard their echoing hoofs,
Past the walls of mossy stone;
The roan flew on at a staggering pace,
But blood is better than bone.
I patted old Kate and gave her the spur,
For I knew it was all my own.

But trample! trample! came their steeds,
I saw their wolf's eyes burn;
I felt like a royal hart at bay,
And made me ready to turn.
I looked where highest grew the may,
And deepest arched the fern.

I flew at the first knave's sallow throat;
One blow and he was down,
The second rogue fired twice and missed;
I sliced the villain's crown,
Clove through the rest, and flogged brave Kate,
Fast, fast to Salisbury town.

Pad! pad! they came on the level sward,
Thud! thud! upon the sand;
With a gleam of swords, and a burning match,
And a shaking of flag and hand:
But one long bound, and I passed the gate,
Safe from the canting band.

BY G. W. THORNBURY.

A NORSE SAGA

Thor and Loki, accompanied by their servant Thialfi, set out on a long and dangerous journey from Asgard, the city of the Norse gods to Utgard's kingdom in the far Northlands. First they sailed across a wide stretch of sea and then journeyed through a cold, bleak, dismal land. Thereafter they crossed great ranges of mountains and, in several places, had to make their way among scattered and strangely-shaped rocks which, through the mist, appeared to them to be the ghost-like figures of huge men, and once, for a day, they wandered through a thick tangled forest.

A T last, after many days of weary trudging and climbing, the three companions came to the edge of a vast barren plain, in the centre of which stood a great city, whose outer walls were so high and forbidding, that Thor knew they had reached the object of their search. Despite the enormous height of the surrounding wall of the city, the adventurers were quite undaunted and approached the entrance, but found that the gates were closed and barred. This however did not stop their progress, for the spaces between the upright bars were so wide that all three passed through quite easily. They found themselves in a long, wide, deserted street, at the other end of which was a very imposing building, much higher than the rest. On advancing towards it they saw that its doors were wide open and they could hear the sound of revelry from within.

Thor and his friends ascended the steps and, on crossing the threshold, beheld an immense banqueting hall, down the middle of which stretched a massive stone table. Huge stone chairs surrounded the table and seated in each was a warrior. Thor quickly glanced round the assembled company and noticed that one among them sat on a raised seat and appeared to be the chief. He approached and paid his greetings.

The chief stared at him, and, without rising, said in a somewhat careless manner: "It is I think, a foolish custom to trouble tired travellers with inquisitive questions about their journey. I know, without asking, that you are Thor from Asgard. It is the custom here that no one shall sit down to table till he has performed some wonderful feat. Let us hear what you and your friends are famed for, and in what way you choose to prove yourselves worthy to sit in our company."

At this speech, Loki, who had cautiously entered the hall behind Thor, pushed himself forward and said, "The feat for which I am best known is eating, and it is one which I am at this moment inclined to perform with right good will. Place food in front of me, and we shall see if any of your followers can despatch it as quickly as I can."

"The feat of which you speak is by no means to be despised," answered the king, "and Logi will be glad to try his powers against yours." A tall, thin, yellow-faced man then approached and a large trough of meat was brought and placed in the middle of the hall. At a given signal, Loki started eating from one end and Logi from the other. The warriors all turned to watch them and a few moments later the two contestants met at the middle of the trough. At first it looked as though both had eaten exactly the same amount, but, when the

trough was examined, it was discovered that Loki had
eaten all the meat in his half and that Logi had not only
eaten the meat but the bones as well. The warriors
nodded their heads and declared that Loki had been
fairly beaten but not disgraced.

Turning next to Thialfi, the king asked him what feat
he proposed to show them.

"In my country I was thought very swift of foot,"
answered Thialfi, "and I will, if you so desire, try a
race with anyone here."

"You have chosen a noble sport, indeed," said the
king, "but you will be a good runner to beat Hugi."

After calling to a tall, slender servant at the end of the
hall, the whole company went outside and proceeded to
a flat, open space nearby. The running distance and
winning post were soon decided and both runners prepared themselves for the race. Then, when they were
ready, the king gave the signal to start.

Thialfi ran fast—as fast as the reindeer when he hears
the wolves howling behind him—but Hugi ran so much
faster that, passing the winning line, he turned round and
met Thialfi about halfway on his course.

"Try again," cried the king; and Thialfi, once more
taking his place, flew along the course with his feet

scarcely touching the ground—as swiftly as an eagle when he swoops on his prey; but with all his effort he was still a good distance from the winning post when Hugi reached it.

"You are certainly a good runner," said the king, "but if you mean to win this race, you must do better unless, perhaps you want to surprise us this time."

The third time, however, Thialfi was wearied and though he did his level best, Hugi, after reaching the goal, turned and met him not far from the starting point.

The warriors then declared Hugi the winner and said there was no need of a further trial.

It was now Thor's turn and the king asked him by what feat he chose to distinguish himself.

"I will try a drinking match with any of you," said Thor.

King Utgard appeared pleased with his choice and when the warriors had returned and resumed their seats in the hall, he ordered one of his servants to bring in his guest's drinking cup.

"There," he said, handing the vessel to Thor, "we will say that you have drunk well if you can empty it in three draughts."

Thor looked into the cup and saw that it contained a green coloured mead. Being very thirsty, he thought to empty it with one gulp, but after a good hearty pull, he saw that he had made very little impression on the amount of liquid in the vessel.

This caused the king to exclaim, "Ha! I do believe that you are reserving your strength for the next two pulls."

Without answering, Thor lifted the cup and drank again until his breath almost failed; but when he put down the drinking vessel, he noticed that the level of the wine had not sunk much.

"If you mean to drink it all in three gulps," said Utgard, "you are leaving yourself a very unfair share for your third and last attempt. I am afraid that if you do not perform better than you have so far, we shall not think much of your prowess here."

Thor felt extremely angry and seizing the cup again, he drank for the third time, much deeper and longer than before; but when he had finished and set the vessel on the table, he noticed that it was still more than half-full. Wearied and disappointed, he said that he would try no more.

"It is now quite clear," said the king, looking round at the company, "that the great Thor from Asgard can do nothing out of the ordinary."

"If you wish," replied Thor, hurt by this remark, "I am willing to attempt any other feat, which you may set me."

"Very well," said the king, "we have a game at which our children play and we are all curious to see how you fare at it. The task is nothing more than to lift my cat from the floor—a childish amusement you will agree."

As he spoke a large grey cat sprang into the hall, mewing and purring after the fashion of his kind. Thor, stooping forward, put his hand under the creature to lift it, but though he tugged and pulled with all his strength, the utmost he could do was to raise one of the cat's paws from the ground.

"Just as I thought," said king Utgard, looking round with a smile.

Thor on hearing this remark, cried, "who is there among you who will dare wrestle with me in my anger?"

"I don't think there is anyone here who would choose to wrestle with you," replied the king, "but if wrestle you must, I will call for Elli. She had laid low many a better man than you have proved yourself to be."

Elli was a withered and toothless old crone and Thor shrank from the thought of wrestling with her. However, he soon found that he had no choice in the matter, for the old woman advanced towards him and held him

almost helpless in her powerful arms. They swayed and
struggled for a few minutes and though Thor strove
bravely, a strange feeling of weakness and weariness
came over him, and he tottered and fell on one knee
before her. At this sight, the warriors laughed aloud and
Utgard, approaching the contestants, requested the old
woman to leave the hall, and proclaimed the trials over.

Despite their lack of success in the tests, the king then
invited Thor and his companions to spend the night
with him as his guests. Thor, though feeling somewhat
humiliated, accepted the courteous invitation, and showed
by his agreeable behaviour during the evening, that he
could lose with good grace.

On the following morning, when Thor and his two
friends were leaving, the king himself accompanied them
outside the city. Before bidding them farewell, Utgard
said, "Now, Thor, tell me truly, before you go, how you
have enjoyed your visit here?"

"I confess," answered Thor, "that in this place, I
have been proved to be a weakling and it will be said that
Thor of Asgard is a person of little worth."

"Indeed, no," cried the king heartily, "far from it.
If I had known what a mighty man of valour you really
are, you would not have been allowed to enter our city.

You see, we were deceiving you by our enchantments in the contests in which you and your companions were engaged last night. When Loki and Logi sat to eat what was in the trough, Loki performed remarkably well, but Logi is fire, who, with eager consuming tongue, licked up both meat and bones. Thialfi," he continued, "must certainly be the swiftest of mortal runners. But, the slender lad, Hugi, was my thought; and what speed can ever equal his?"

"Lastly, in your own trials, you little knew what wonderful feats you were performing. The other end of that drinking horn stretched to the ocean and when you reach the shore, you will see how much the deep sea itself has been diminished by your draughts. Here-after, men watching the going out of the tide will call it the ebb or draught of Thor. Scarcely less wonderful was the prowess you displayed in the second trial. What appeared to you to be an old grey cat, was in reality, the serpent which encircles the earth. When we saw that you had succeeded in moving it, we were afraid that the foundations of the world would be shaken by your tremendous strength. Nor need you be ashamed of having been overthrown by the old crone Elli, for she is old age, and there never has, and never will be, anyone whom she cannot lay low. Well, we must part now and I hope you will not come here again or attempt anything against our city, for we shall defend it with even greater enchantments."

At these words, Thor raised his famous hammer, Miolner, and was about to challenge the king to a fresh trial of strength, but, before he could say a word, the king of the Northlands vanished from his sight. Turning round to look for the city, he found that it too, had disappeared, and that he, Loki and Thialfi, were alone again on the great, barren plain.

(Adapted from "*Heroes of Asgard*" by A. and E. KEARY.)

INTERESTING FACTS
ABOUT NORWAY

1. Before the coming of Christianity, the people of Northern Europe worshipped gods and heroes in the same manner as the Greeks and Romans, and many of their legends are alike in praising wisdom and bravery. The chief of the northern gods was *Odin* or Woden and our Wednesday means "Woden's day". *Thor*, the god of thunder, who gave his name to Thursday ("Thor's day") and *Loki*, the mischief-maker, are next in prominence. The gods sat in council in the beautiful city of *Asgard*, which was situated on the top of a lofty mountain.

2. The Northmen or *Norsemen* lived in *Scandinavia*, a name given to the peninsula which includes Norway and Sweden. For a long time the Danes were overlords of the North, but in 1814, Norway regained its freedom. In the same year however, Norway was forced into union with Sweden under *Bernadotte*, one of Napoleon's generals. The bonds between the two countries were severed in 1905, and since then Norway has been a kingdom by itself. In *Oslo*, the capital, formerly called Christiania, are situated the *"Storting"* or Parliament buildings and the famous *National Museum*.

3. Norway ("The Northern Way"), is a very mountainous country and deep, long, narrow arms of the sea, called *fjords* or viks, wind their way into the steep, rocky coast. *Sognefjord* is the longest, stretching 106 miles

from the sea. *The Gulf Stream*, a warm current in the
Atlantic Ocean, washes its shores and consequently the
climate of Norway is not so bitterly cold as other regions
so far north. This warm Atlantic drift keeps the northern
ports free from ice. The *"maelstrom"* is a dreaded
whirlpool that lies at the southern tip of the *Lofoten
Islands*; it is dangerous for small craft to approach its
waters. The mountains cause roads and railways to
turn and twist, so that travel in winter is difficult unless
by sea.

4. The *Vikings* or "Men of the Viks" were the old
sea-rovers, who, for centuries, plundered the coasts of
Europe. They were striking warriors in their ox-horned
helmets and short coats of mail; they were armed with
such weapons as shields, spears, axes and swords. They

journeyed to many far-off
lands, some settling in *Normandy*, the isles of *Scotland,
Iceland* and *Greenland*. A
famous Viking, *Leif Eriksson*
is credited with landing on
the shores of Canada and
even sailing as far south as
the Hudson River where his
people settled for a time at
the end of the tenth century.

5. In the green patches of the deep valleys of Norway may be seen snug little villages consisting of brightly painted, wooden farmhouses, known as *"gaards"*. In summer, the cattle are sent to graze on the high pastures far up the mountain sides while the guardians of the herds, usually girls, live in huts called *"saeters"*. The girls use a long horn called a *"lur"* to call from one mountain-

pasture to another. The lur is made of birchbark wound round a hollow wooden stick. The animals wear bells round their necks so that they can be easily found when wanted. In autumn, hay and moss are gathered, dried on racks and placed in huge barns for winter food.

6. Norway has many forests of pine and fir trees, and from these a valuable supply of *timber* is obtained. Great progress has been made in the wood industries, for besides paper-mills, factories have been built which manufacture window-frames, doors and gates and ship them to other countries. The swift-flowing mountain streams provide abundant *electric power* for factories, homes and electric railways.

7. The Norwegians, largely because of Norway's geographical position, have always been great seafarers, and fishing remains still a major occupation of the people. The Lofoten Islands serve as a base for the boats engaged in *herring* and *cod* fishing. The *liver oil* extracted from the cod is a valuable product. Around *Stavanger* brisling *sardines* are caught and thousands of cans are exported each year. The headquarters of the great fishing fleets is at *Bergen*, the chief fish marketing port of Norway. In the market, some fish are kept in tanks, so that buyers can choose their fish alive.

8. Norway is sometimes called *"The Land of the Midnight Sun"* and many people visit the country to witness this remarkable sight. For a period in summer the sun does not set, thus giving continuous daylight for some weeks. In winter, however, the opposite process takes place and there are weeks of continuous darkness. Another amazing sight is the *"Aurora Borealis"* or "Northern Lights". Bright rays of blue, green, violet and orange appear in all parts of the night sky creating a strange and beautiful spectacle. The most northerly point of the country is *North Cape*, which rises a thousand feet almost sheer out of the sea; it is the home of thousands of seabirds.

9. Parents love to recount tales of the Vikings to their children and nothing pleases the boys and girls more than to hear exciting stories of their adventurous ancestors. At meal-times, a table in the centre of the room holds a great many dishes of meat, fish and vegetables, from which one helps oneself. This is called *"smorgasbord"* and it is often the first course of a meal. Snow sports are a feature of winter life and *ski-ing* and *sledging* are very popular. The children are experts at these sports, and an unusual sledge like a chair on runners, called a *"spark-stotting"* is used by elder brothers and sisters to convey the younger members of the family to school over the snow.

10. In the far north of Norway lives a small hardy race known as the *Lapps*. They are a nomadic people, dwelling in tents and wandering about from place to place. *Reindeer* provide them with food, milk and clothing but are useful also as beasts of burden. So useful and necessary are these animals that a Laplander's wealth is judged by the number he possesses. The Norwegian *elkhound* is a friendly animal although it is a fearless hunter. As its name suggests, this dog was originally used for hunting the elk of northern Europe.

QUESTIONS ON THE STORY

1. Name the three companions in the story.
2. From what city did they set out?
3. What was their destination?
4. Explain why the closed gates did not stop their progress.
5. Describe the banqueting hall.
6. What was the custom before sitting at the table?
7. What feat did Loki wish to perform?
8. Describe the contest in detail.
9. By what feat did Thialfi attempt to show his prowess?
10. Describe the manner in which he was defeated.
11. By what feat did Thor choose to distinguish himself?
12. What happened when the mead was brought?
13. What was the king's name?
14. What trial did the king set Thor?
15. Describe what happened in this test.
16. What was Thor's challenge to the warriors?
17. Who opposed him and what was the outcome?
18. What was represented by (*a*) Logi; (*b*) Hugi?
19. What did the following enchantments mean: (*a*) the green coloured mead; (*b*) the old crone Elli?
20. What was the name of Thor's famous hammer?

QUESTIONS ON THE INTERESTING FACTS

1. (a) Name two famous Norse gods and how are their names still kept alive?
   (b) Where did the gods sit in council?

2. (a) What name is given to the peninsula which includes Norway and Sweden?
   (b) Who were overlords of the North for a long time?
   (c) What is the name of the Norwegian Houses of Parliament?

3. (a) What name is given to the deep, long, narrow arms of the sea?
   (b) What warm current washes against the shores of Norway?
   (c) What is the "maelstrom"?

4. (a) Describe a Viking warrior.
   (b) Name the Viking who is credited with the discovery of America.

5. (a) What happens to the cattle in summer?
   (b) Why do the animals have bells on their necks?

6. (a) Name some of the things made from Norwegian timber.
   (b) Why are the swift mountain streams important to Norway?

7. (a) Name the places in Norway that are noted for fishing.
   (b) Why is the housewife in Bergen always able to buy fresh fish?

8. (a) Name two remarkable sights to be seen in Norway.
   (b) What is the most northerly tip of the country?

9. (a) What stories do Norwegian boys and girls like to hear?
   (b) Name two winter sports in Norway.

10. (*a*) What is the name of the people who inhabit Northern Norway?
    (*b*) On what is their wealth usually judged?
    (*c*) Name a Norwegian dog.

DEVELOPMENT EXERCISES

1. Point out on the map of Norway (*a*) Oslo; (*b*) North Cape; (*c*) Bergen; (*d*) Lofoten Islands; (*e*) Stavanger.

2. EITHER (*a*) Give a short account of a feat performed by one of the companions and its meaning.
   OR (*b*) Describe briefly a Viking raid on the western isles of Scotland.

3. This story is called a saga, which is an old Norse folk tale. Write a sentence to illustrate the meaning of each of the following: (*a*) novel; (*b*) diary; (*c*) epistle; (*d*) biography; (*e*) essay.

4. Cats figure prominently in folklore. Explain the meaning of the following sentences: (*a*) When the cat is away, the mice will play; (*b*) Those two people are leading a cat-and-dog life; (*c*) The deserter was given the cat-o'-nine tails as punishment; (*d*) She was such a gossip that she let the cat out of the bag; (*e*) Yesterday it rained cats and dogs.

5. Give a short description of the "Land of the Midnight Sun."

6. "*Smorgasbord*" is usually the first course of a meal in Norway. If you were dining in a restaurant, what would the following terms signify: (*a*) hors d'oevre; (*b*) dessert; (*c*) consomme; (*d*) à la carte; (*e*) entrée?

7. What do each of the following Norse words mean:
   (*a*) gaard; (*b*) vik; (*c*) saeter; (*d*) lur; (*e*) spark-
   stotting?
8. Make a full list of winter sports.

THE VIRTUOUS ONE

*"The Small Woman" by Alan Burgess recounts the true
story of Gladys Aylward, the London parlourmaid,
who overcame all obstacles to become a missionary in
North China. After many hardships, she met Mrs.
Jeannie Lawson, a Scots missionary, and together they
started a Christian settlement which they called "The
Inn of Eight Happinesses". The following is an adaptation of an event which took place shortly after Mrs.
Lawson's death, when Gladys was in sole charge
of the Inn.*

THERE arrived during her second year at Yangcheng,
a pleasant young man called Lu-Yung-Cheng, He
and Gladys were standing in the courtyard when a
messenger from the Mandarin rushed in waving a piece
of scarlet paper. He gabbled at such a rate that Gladys
found it difficult to understand him.

"What's the paper for, anyway?" she asked Lu-Yung-
Cheng.

"It's an official summons from the Mandarin" said
Lu-Yung-Cheng nervously. "A riot has broken out in
the men's prison."

"You must come at once," said the messenger urgently.
"It is most important!"

Gladys stared at him. "But what's the riot in the prison
got to do with us?"

"You must come at once!" repeated the messenger

loudly. "It is an official order." He hopped from one foot to the other in impatience.

Lu-Yung-Cheng looked at her doubtfully. "When that piece of red paper arrives from the Mandarin, you must go." There was a nervous tremor in his voice.

"All right, *you* go and see what it's all about," said Gladys. "It's obviously a man's job. I know nothing about prisons. I've never been in one in my life . . . though I really don't see what you're supposed to do."

She could see from Lu-Yung-Cheng's face that the prospect did not appeal to him.

"Hurry, please hurry!" cried the messenger.

Reluctantly Lu-Yung-Cheng trailed after him to the door. Gladys watched him reach the opening, take a quick look behind at her, then dodge swiftly to the left as the messenger turned to the right. She could hear the sound of his running feet as he tore down the road.

Within two seconds the messenger discovered his loss. He stormed back through the doorway crying "Ai-ee-ee!" and shaking his fist in rage. He raced across the court-yard, a little fat man without dignity, towards Gladys.

"Now, *you* must come," he shouted. "This is an official paper. You are ordered to come. You *must* come. Now! With me! If you refuse you will get into trouble!"

"All right," she said mildly. "I'll come. I really don't know what's the matter with Lu-Yung-Cheng. He must feel ill or something. But I certainly don't see what a riot in the prison has to do with me . . ."

They hurried up the road and in through the East Gate. A few yards inside the gate the blank outside wall of the prison flanked the main street. From the other side came screams, shouts, yells, the most horrible noises.

"My goodness!" said Gladys. "It certainly is a riot, isn't it?"

The Governor of the prison, small, pale-faced, his

mouth set in a worried line, met her at the entrance. Behind were grouped half a dozen of his staff.

"We are glad you have come," he said quickly. "There is a riot in the prison; the convicts are killing each other."

"So I can hear," she said. "But what am I here for? I'm only the missionary woman. Why don't you send the soldiers in to stop it?"

"The convicts are murderers, bandits, thieves," said the Governor, his voice trembling. "The soldiers are frightened. There are not enough of them."

"I'm sorry to hear that," said Gladys. "But what do you expect me to do about it? I don't even know why you asked me to come . . ."

The Governor stepped forward. "You must go in and stop the fighting."

"I must go in . . .!" Gladys' mouth dropped open; her eyes rounded in utter amazement. "Me! Me go in there! Are you mad? If I went in they'd kill me!"

The Governor's eyes were fixed on her. "But how can they kill you? You tell everybody that you have come here because you have the living God inside you . . ."

"*The living God*?" she stammered.

"You preach it everywhere—in the streets and villages. If you preach the truth, if your God protects you from harm, then you can stop this riot."

Gladys stared at him. Her mind raced round in bewilderment, searching for some fact that would explain her beliefs to this simple, deluded man. A little cell in her mind kept blinking on and off with an urgent semaphore message; "It's true! You have been preaching that your Christian God protects you from harm. Fail now, and you are finished in Yangcheng. Discard your faith now, and you discard it for ever!" It was a desperate challenge. But how could she go into the prison? Those men—murderers, thieves, bandits, rioting and killing each other inside those walls! How could she . . .? "I must try," she said to herself. "I must try. O God give me strength."

She looked up at the Governor's pale face, knowing that now hers was the same colour. "All right," she said. "Open the door. I'll go in to them." She did not trust her voice to say any more.

"The key!" snapped the Governor. "The key, quickly.'

One of his orderlies came forward with a huge iron key; soon the immense iron-barred door swung open. The door closed behind her. She heard the great key turn. She was locked in the prison with a horde of raving criminals, who sounded by their din as if they had all gone completely insane. With faltering footsteps she walked forward and came to an abrupt standstill, rooted in horror.

The courtyard was about sixty feet square, with queer cage-like structures round all four sides. Within its confines a writhing, fiendish battle was going on. Several bodies were stretched out on the flagstones. One man, obviously dead, lay only a few feet away from her. The main group of men, however, were watching one convict who brandished a large, blood-stained chopper. As she stared, he suddenly rushed at them and they scattered wildly to every part of the square. No one took any notice whatsoever of Gladys as she stood

motionless. The man rushed again; the group parted; he singled one man out and chased him. The man ran towards Gladys, then ducked away. The madman with the axe halted only a few feet from her. Without any instinctive plan, hardly realising what she was doing, she took two angry steps towards him.

"Give me that chopper," she said furiously. "Give it to me at once!"

The man turned to look at her. For three long seconds the wild dark pupils staring from bloodshot eyes glared at her. He took two paces forward. Suddenly, meekly, he held out the axe. Gladys snatched the weapon from his hand and held it rigidly down by her side. The other convicts—there must have been fifty or sixty cowering there—stared from every corner of the courtyard. All action was frozen and Gladys knew she must clinch her advantage.

"All of you!" she shouted. "Come over here. Come on, form into a line! You, over there! Come on, form up in front of me!"

Obediently the convicts shambled across, forming into a ragged group before her. She regarded them stormily. There was silence. Then suddenly her fear had gone. They were so wretched. They were so hopeless. She could have wept openly that human creatures could be so wretched. With an effort, she tightened her lips and took command again. The fear had gone, yes; but she knew that she must cow them with her authority.

"You should be ashamed of yourselves," she said, berating them like an irate mother scolding a crowd of naughty children. "All this noise and all this mess! The governor sent me in here to find out what it was all about. Now if you clean up this courtyard and promise to behave in future, I'll ask him to deal leniently with you this time. Now, what is your grievance? Why did you start fighting like this?"

There was no answer. Several hung their heads in shame.

"I want you to appoint a spokesman, then," she went on. "He can tell me what the trouble is, and then you can start cleaning up the courtyard at once. Now go over in that corner and appoint your spokesman. I'll wait here."

The convicts trooped over into the corner she indicated and talked among themselves. A few moments later, one of the taller men of slightly better physique approached. Like the others, he was dressed in rags.

"My name is Feng," he said. "I am their spokesman."

Gladys listened to his story. Later she learned that he had once been a Buddhist priest; he had been convicted of theft from the other priests in the temple and sentenced to eight years in gaol. He explained that no one really knew why, or how, the riot had started. They were allowed the chopper for an hour each day to cut up their food. Someone had quarrelled over its possession and someone else had joined in. He could not explain this strange occurrence. Perhaps it was that many of the men had been there for many years, he said. As she knew, unless their friends or relatives sent in food, they starved. It was hard to sit up against a wall and starve to death while other men ate. He could not explain the outbreak, but the walls were high and the doors were strong; they never saw the outside world, women or the mountains, a tree in blossom or a friendly face; sometimes the spirit grew so oppressed that it burst out in a wild tumult of violence. That, he thought, is what had occurred. They were all very sorry.

"What do you do all day in here?" asked Gladys seriously.

"Do? There is nothing to do."

"No occupation of any sort?"

"None!"

"But a man must have work, something to do. I shall see the Governor about it."

It was at this moment she became conscious that the Governor and his retinue were behind her. The noise of the riot had died, and they had now thought it safe to enter and take an official part in the peace treaty.

The Governor bowed to Gladys. "You have done well. We must thank you," he said gratefully.

"It's disgraceful," she said bitterly. "These men are locked up here week after week, year after year, with nothing to do. Of course you have riots if they've nothing to occupy their time. They must have work to do. We must get looms so they can weave cloth; we must find them all sorts of jobs so that they can earn a little money and buy food, and get back a little self-respect."

The Governor nodded. Whether he agreed or not she could not tell.

"We will discuss it later," he said amiably.

"I have promised them there will be no reprisals," she said.

The Governor nodded again. A few corpses were rarely the subject of an official inquiry in the Chinese penal system. "As long as there is no recurrence," he said, "we shall forget all about it."

"That is good," said Gladys. She turned to Feng. "I'm going now, but I shall come back. I promise I will do all I can to help you."

She saw upon her the dark eyes of the priest who was a thief. "Thank you," he said. "Thank you, Ai-weh-deh."

She did not know at the time what the word "Ai-weh-deh" meant. That evening she asked Lu-Yung-Cheng when he returned from the long walk he had so suddenly decided to take.

"Ai-weh-deh?" he said curiously. "It means the virtuous one."

She was known as Ai-weh-deh for all her remaining years in China.

QUESTIONS ON THE STORY

1. From what story is the extract taken?
2. What was Gladys Aylward before she became a missionary?
3. What was the name of the inn?
4. How long had she been at Yangcheng?
5. From whom did the messenger come?
6. What did the messenger say?
7. Why did Lu-Yung-Cheng dodge the messenger?
8. Who was waiting for Gladys at the prison?
9. What did he ask her to do?
10. Why did he ask her to do this?
11. Describe the scene in the prison courtyard.
12. From whom were the prisoners running?
13. Tell how Gladys brought him under control.
14. What did she make the prisoners do?
15. What did she promise them?
16. Why was Feng in prison?
17. What was his explanation of the riot?
18. What did Gladys ask the governor to do for the prisoners?
19. What condition did the governor make for the promise of no reprisals?
20. What name did Feng give to Gladys?

DEVELOPMENT EXERCISES

1. Describe the route from London to North China (*a*) by sea; (*b*) by land.

2. You have just read the story of a riot. Find out information on (*a*) the Riot Act; (*b*) some famous riots and their causes.

3. Gladys Aylward was a missionary in North China. Find out what you can of the following missionaries and the places with which they are connected: (*a*) David Livingstone; (*b*) Saint Columba; (*c*) Father Damien; (*d*) Saint Augustine; (*e*) Albert Schweitzer.

4. People in a prison are called convicts. What do we call the people (*a*) in a hospital; (*b*) in a church; (*c*) at a concert; (*d*) in a play; (*e*) at a football match?

5. A person who weaves cloth is a weaver. What name do we give to each of the following; (*a*) one who mends shoes; (*d*) a woman who tends the sick; (*c*) one who pulls teeth; (*d*) a man who makes clothes; (*e*) a woman who sews cloth?

6. A mandarin was an important official in China. Find out what the following titles signify and in what countries they may be found: (*a*) commissar; (*b*) begum; (*c*) khedive; (*d*) sultana; (*e*) maharajah?

7. The Inn of the Eight Happinesses was set up to attend to the needs of travellers. Give some names for present-day places of rest and refreshment.

8. Ai-weh-deh was the Chinese nickname for Gladys Aylward. With what places are the following nicknames associated: (*a*) Cockney; (*b*) Jock; (*c*) Taffy; (*d*) Geordie; (*e*) Paddy; (*f*) Aussie; (*g*) Kiwi?

THE CYCLONE

The following extract has been abridged from Frank T. Bullen's "The Cruise of the Cachalot", a modern classic of adventure at sea. This book tells the story of a South-Sea Whaler engaged in hunting "cachalots" another name for sperm-whales. Up until the time of the adventure related below, the expedition had been favoured with fair weather. But now their luck was to change.

A CHANGE was now evidently coming fast. Of course, we forward had no access to the barometer; not that we should have understood its indications if we had seen it, but we all knew that something was going to be radically wrong with the weather. For instead of the lovely blue of the sky we had been so long accustomed to by day and night, a nasty, greasy shade had come over the heavens, which, reflected in the sea, made that look dirty and stale also. That well known appearance of the waves before a storm was also very marked, which consists of an undecided sort of break in their tops. Instead of running regularly, they seemed to hunch themselves up in little heaps, and throw off a tiny flutter of spray, which generally fell in the opposite direction to what little wind there was. The pigs and fowls felt the approaching change keenly, and showed the greatest uneasiness, leaving their food and acting strangely.

We were making scarcely any headway, so that the

storm was longer making its appearance than it would have been had we been a swift clipper ship running down the Indian Ocean. For two days we were kept in suspense; but on the second night the gloom began to deepen, the wind to moan, and a very uncomfortable "jobble" of a sea got up. Extra "gaskets" were put upon the sails, and everything movable about the decks was made as secure as it could be. Only the two close-reefed topsails and two storm stay-sails were carried, so that we were in excellent trim for fighting the bad weather when it did come. The sky gradually darkened and took on a bright green tint, the effect of which was most peculiar.

' The wind blew fitfully in short gusts, veering continually back and forth over about a quarter of the compass. Although it was still light, it kept up a constant mournful moan not to be accounted for in any way. Darker and darker grew the heavens although no clouds were visible, only a general pall of darkness. Glimmering lightnings played continually about the eastern horizon, but not brilliant enough to show us the approaching storm-cloud and so came the morning of the third day from the beginning of the change.

But for the clock we would hardly have known that day had broken, so gloomy and dark was the sky. At last light came in the east, but such a light as no-one would wish to see: it was, more properly, a wind glare. Then, beneath it we saw the mountainous clouds fringed with dull violet and with jagged sabres of lightning darting from their solid black bosoms. The wind began to rise steadily but rapidly, so that by eight a.m. it was blowing a furious gale from E.N.E.

The roar of the wind now dominated every sound, so that it might have been thundering furiously, but we should not have heard it. The ship still maintained her splendid character as a sea-boat, hardly shipping a drop of water; but she lay over at a most distressing angle, her deck sloping off fully thirty-five to forty degrees. Fortunately, she did not roll to windward. It may have been raining in perfect torrents, but the tempest tore off the surface of the sea, and sent it in massive sheets continually flying over us, so that we could not possibly have distinguished between fresh water and salt.

The chief anxiety was for the safety of the boats. Early on the second day of warning they had been hoisted to the topmost notch of the cranes, and secured as thoroughly as experience could suggest; but at every lurch we gave it seemed as if we must dip them under water, while the wind threatened to stave the weather ones in by its actual solid weight. It was now blowing a furious cyclone, the force of which was almost unbelievable.

The terrible day wore on, without any lightening of the tempest, till noon, when the wind suddenly fell to a calm. Until that time, the sea, although heavy, was not vicious or irregular, and we had not shipped any heavy water at all. But when the force of the wind was suddenly withdrawn, such a sea arose as I have never seen before or since. Inky mountains of water

smashing one another in whirlpools of foam; our staunch and seaworthy ship was tossed and twirled in the maddened grip of the sea.

It was quite impossible to loose one's hold and attempt to do anything without running the risk of being dashed to pieces. Our decks were full of water now, for it tumbled on board at all points; but as yet no serious damage had been done. Such a miracle as that could not be expected to continue for long. Suddenly a warning shout rang out from somewhere—"Hold on all, for your lives!" Out of the hideous turmoil around arose an awful heap of water. Higher and higher it towered, until it was level with our lower yards, then it broke and fell upon us. All was blank. Beneath that mass every thought, every feeling, fled but one—"How long shall I be able to hold my breath?" After what seemed a never-ending time, we emerged from the wave more dead than alive, but with the good ship still staunch underneath us. But, alas for others!—men, like ourselves, whose hopes were gone. Quite near us was the battered remainder of what had been a splendid ship. Her masts were gone, not even the stumps being visible, and it seemed to our eager eyes as if she was settling down. It was even so, for as we looked, unmindful of our own danger, she quietly disappeared—swallowed up with her human cargo in a moment, like a pebble dropped into a pond.

While we looked with hardly beating hearts at the place where she had sunk, all was blotted out in thick darkness again. With a roar, as of a thousand thunders, the tempest came once more, but from the opposite direction now. As we were under no sail, we ran little risk of being caught aback; but, even had we, nothing could have been done, the vessel being utterly out of control, besides the impossibility of turning about. It so happened, however, that when the storm burst upon us again, we were stern on to it, and we drove steadily for a few moments until we had time to haul to the wind again. Great heavens! Now it blew! Surely, I thought, this cannot last long—just as we sometimes say of the rain when it is extra heavy. It did last, however, for what seemed a never-ending time, although anyone could see that the sky was getting kindlier. Gradually, almost without our realising it, it took off, the sky cleared, and the tumult ceased, until a new day broke in all its beauty over a re-born world.

Years afterwards I read, in one of the hand-books treating of hurricanes and cyclones, that "in the centre of these revolving storms the sea is so violent that few ships can pass through it and live." That is true. I have been there, and bear witness that but for the build and sea-kindliness of the "Cachalot", she could not have come out of that horrible cauldron again, but would have joined the nameless unfortunate whom we saw perish, "never again heard of."

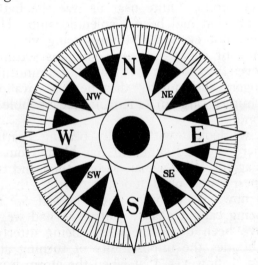

QUESTIONS ON THE STORY

1. What does the word "cachalot" mean?
2. In what way could the storm be forecast by looking at the sky?
3. Describe the appearance of the waves.
4. How did the animals behave?
5. Why was the storm so long in coming?
6. What precautions were taken?
7. Describe how the sky changed its colour.
8. Describe how the wind changed.
9. In what direction could flashes of lightning be seen?
10. In what way was the light unpleasant to look at?
11. From what direction was the gale blowing?
12. Are we told that the ship itself was in difficulties in the gale?
13. What was the chief source of anxiety?
14. What happened to the wind at noon? What else happened?
15. What effect on the ship did the heavy sea have?
16. Why did a warning-shout ring out?
17. What was the one thought in every sailor's mind?
18. What sight greeted their eyes on emerging from the wave?
19. To what is the sinking ship likened?
20. When the storm burst again, how was the ship placed?

KETCH

CATAMARAN

SCHOONER

DINGHY

SLOOP

SAILING BARGE

CUTTER

YAWL

THE PANAMA CANAL

The story that lies behind the building of the Panama Canal goes back to the time when the Spanish conqueror Balboa crossed the mountains of the Darien isthmus in 1513, and first looked on the Pacific and Atlantic Oceans. To join both oceans together was then no more than a dream; to make that dream come true was to take another four hundred years and the finest resources of engineering and medicine, as well as a vast amount of money and labour.

IN 1695, a Scotsman, William Paterson, who was responsible for founding the Bank of England, had the idea of establishing a colony on the isthmus of Darien or Panama, where it would command a trade link between the two oceans. The scheme, however, was a complete failure owing to the unhealthy climate and the hostility of the Spaniards, so that a valuable chance of some contact between the Atlantic and the Pacific at this time was lost. Such a state of isolation for each ocean lasted about 150 years.

Although a railway spanned the isthmus in 1853, a fresh but vain attempt to join the two oceans was made in 1889 by Ferdinand de Lesseps, the Frenchman who had built the Suez Canal. The work of construction at Panama was entirely different from that at Suez however, and when landslides, floods and malaria had brought work almost to a standstill, the project was abandoned.

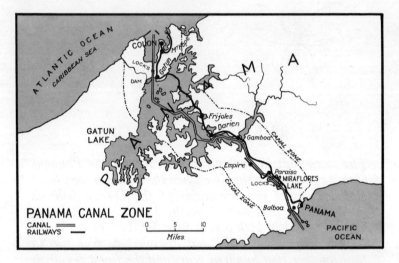

PANAMA CANAL ZONE

The benefits that a canal across the forty mile wide isthmus could bring, persisted in people's minds and in 1903 the United States government bought the rights of a ten-mile wide zone across Panama. The task had begun in earnest and the developments of man were brought into combat with the forces of nature.

It was found that the dreaded mosquitoes which breed in swamps and which carry malaria germs, could be destroyed by spreading oil over the swamps and stagnant waters. The larvae of the mosquito live below water but need air to live, so when the oil stopped the air the larvae died. Thus ended a deadly scourge which had played a major part in causing the failure of previous attempts. Sanitary houses and hospitals were erected, cleanliness was insisted upon and before work had even started, this section of the tropics had become almost a health resort. The doctor in charge, U.S. Army Colonel William Gorgas even forbade the drinking of alcohol in the zone so that the workmen would be completely fit for their job.

Two large artificial lakes were constructed, one at Gatun and the other at Miraflores, and these formed dams for the torrential rivers. As these dams were at different levels, lock gates had to be fixed at each end of the lakes; these lock gates are the biggest in the world. A passage called the Gaillard Cut was made through the Culebra mountains joining the two lakes. On either side, a series of locks brought ships to the level of the ocean, where the approaches had to be deepened to allow the largest vessels to use the canal. The American army engineer-in-chief, Colonel G. W. Goethals in his construction of the Panama Canal completed one of the greatest engineering feats in the history of mankind. This great canal was officially opened for regular traffic in 1914.

In passing through the canal from the Atlantic seaboard to the Pacific Ocean, vessels start from Colon. They are towed by electric locomotives called "mules" which control the speed and course of the ships, and the ships are not allowed to use their own power lest they damage the walls of the canal. Three great locks raise

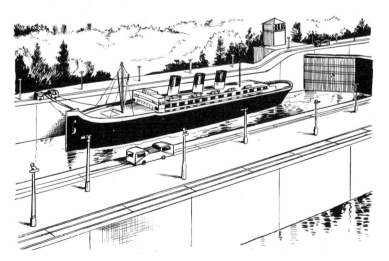

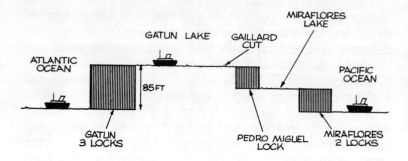

the ship to Gatun Lake, 85 feet above sea-level and then she passes through the Gaillard Cut by one lock to Miraflores Lake, finally descending to Panama on the Pacific Ocean by two more locks. Each of the six locks are in duplicate to allow free passage for ships coming and going. Incidentally, a strange feature of the Panama Canal is that the Pacific end of the canal is not as far west as the Atlantic end.

The advantages that this canal brought to American shipping were tremendous, for sea-routes from one side of the country to the other were shortened by several thousand miles. The ships of Great Britain and other European countries also use this quicker route for trade with New Zealand and the west coast ports of North and South America.

INTERESTING FACTS ABOUT CANALS

1. A *canal* is a man-made waterway that is generally used for purposes of draining land, irrigating land or as a means of transport. Many natural canals, usually called channels or straits, exist throughout the world. They have been formed by low land sinking and the waters on either side joining together. Hundreds of years later, these water passages have broadened considerably and have become vital links in the trade routes of the world. Among many such natural canals are the Straits of Dover, the Straits of Gibraltar, Magellan Straits, Bass Straits, Cook Straits, Bering Straits and the Straits of Malacca.

2. The best examples of canals used for draining land are to be found in *Holland*, where much of the country is below sea-level. The Dutch landscape is dotted with *windmills*, which drive the pumps to drain the surface water from the fields into the canals. Dykes are used to prevent flooding and since the *Zuyder Zee* was enclosed in 1932, over 300,000 acres of land have been reclaimed for farming purposes. In winter the Dutch people use the frozen canals for *ice-skating*.

3. In a hot dry country, such as *Egypt*, water is scarce and to prevent the land from becoming barren, channels are dug from dams on the River Nile for many miles inland. This *irrigation* scheme encourages valuable plant life in desert areas. These canals must be continually kept open, for the Egyptian farms and cotton fields could not exist without these life-lines of water.

4. Many inland waterways are used for the transport of heavy goods by *barges*. This method of carrying materials is not so well-favoured as it used to be, for although it is cheaper, it has the disadvantage of being much slower. Speed is regulated by the number of bridges and locks which the barges encounter, and often the movement of the barges is controlled literally by "horse" power.

5. Many canals in Great Britain are used less and less while others have fallen into disuse altogether. In Scotland, the *Caledonian Canal* which was made simply by joining three lochs together is little used except by fishing craft from the east coast ports going to and from the fishing grounds off the western coast. The *Forth and Clyde Canal* which used to be a highway for barges taking iron ore to the foundries of central Scotland is now closed. The same fate has overtaken many English waterways and even the hundred mile stretch of the *Grand Union Canal* is slowly going out of use.

6. Two notable "short cuts" for ships in Europe are the *Corinth Canal* in Greece and the *Kiel Canal* in Germany. The former was built in 1893 cutting across

the solid rock of the isthmus of Corinth. Overhead bridges from the tops of the steep sides of the canal connect north and south Greece. The Kiel Canal, which also has no locks, was built two years later and it gives the countries of the Baltic Sea quicker access to the west.

7. *Venice*, at the head of the Adriatic Sea, is one of the most fascinating cities of Europe, for it has many canals instead of streets, Long narrow boats with curved ends, called "*gondolas*", ply passengers and goods from one part of the city to another. The gondoliers tie up at mooring posts, which are lit with lanterns at night, making the canals very colourful and romantic. The Doge's Palace on the famous *Grand Canal* is one of the city's most beautiful buildings. A peculiar custom of former days was that the *Doge* or ruler of Venice, used to throw a ring into the water each year to show that the city was wed to the sea.

8. One of the greatest arteries of world trade is the *Suez Canal* separating the two continents of Asia and Africa. As trade with India increased, the overland route across Suez became regular but very expensive. In 1859, the French engineer, *Ferdinand de Lesseps*, started to cut a passage through this flat desert country. Ten years later, the first sea-going ships passed through the canal, which is a hundred miles long, and has no locks, thus completing a direct water route from the North Atlantic to the Indian Ocean. The journey from Port Said at the Mediterranean end to Port Tewfik on the Red Sea, takes about fifteen hours and shortens the distance from Britain to the East by about 4,000 miles. Dredging operations are constantly necessary to keep a way open for ships. The canal belongs to Egypt though it is a vital waterway serving the merchant fleets of many nations.

9. Two well-known Canadian canals, which carry millions of tons of wheat and other commodities, are the *Saulte Ste. Marie* and the *Welland* canals. The former was created to by-pass the rapids between Lakes Superior and Huron, while the latter was built to avoid the Niagara Falls and form a link between lakes Erie and Ontario.

10. The Great Lakes which lie between Canada and the United States have become parts of the world's ocean highways, for it is now possible for big ships to sail up the man-made *Saint Lawrence Seaway* to the busy lake ports of Toronto, Cleveland and Chicago. A 218 mile canal joins the Atlantic with these Great Lakes, which contain half of the fresh water of the world. There are seven locks, five on the Canadian side and two on the United States side of the frontier. Bridges needed to be raised fifty feet to allow big ship traffic to pass and, indeed, from Montreal, these ocean-going vessels are

raised 246 feet above sea-level to Lake Ontario. The Saint Lawrence Seaway carries the world's shipping 2,200 miles inland, half-way across the north American continent and deep into the heart of Canada. This new seaway, which belongs equally to Canada and the United States was officially opened simultaneously by Her Majesty Queen Elizabeth and President Dwight Eisenhower and it has brought increased prosperity to both countries.

QUESTIONS ON THE STORY

1. Who first looked on the Pacific and Atlantic Oceans?
2. What was the Darien Scheme?
3. Name another project that he had started.
4. Give three reasons why the colonists failed.
5. Who also made a vain attempt to construct the Panama Canal?
6. In what ways, do you think, the building of the Suez Canal differed from that of the Panama Canal?
7. What country eventually bought possession of the canal zone?
8. Tell how the malaria germ was conquered.
9. Who was the doctor in charge of medical operations?
10. What rule did he make so that the workmen would be fit for their jobs?
11. Name the two artificial lakes and tell the purpose they served.
12. What was the name of the engineer in charge of the canal construction?
13. Why was it necessary to fix lock gates at the ends of the lakes?
14. Why did the approaches to the canals have to be deepened?

15. When was the canal officially opened for traffic?
16. What are "mules", and for what are they used?
17. Why are ships going through the canal not allowed to use their own power?
18. Why are the locks in duplicate? How many are there altogether?
19. What great benefit does the canal give to American shipping?
20. Explain why the Atlantic end of the canal is further west than the Pacific end.

QUESTIONS ON THE INTERESTING FACTS

1. Name three different types of canals.
2. Holland is sometimes called "the land of Windmills". For what purpose are these windmills used?
3. Explain how water is brought to the farms and cotton fields of Egypt.
4. Why has the transport of goods on canals become less important?
5. How has Manchester, an inland town, become Britain's fourth largest port?
6. Name two important European canals and what seas do they connect?
7. What are Venetian boats called and for what are they used?
8. Why is the Suez Canal most important to Great Britain?
9. Name two important Canadian Canals and the lakes they connect.
10. Why is the Saint Lawrence seaway important and who performed the official opening ceremony?

DEVELOPMENT EXERCISES

1. Point out on a map of
   (a) *Britain*—Caledonian Canal, River Clyde, Straits of Dover, Manchester, River Mersey.
   (b) *Europe*—Corinth Canal, Gibraltar, Kiel Canal Venice, Zuyder Zee.
   (c) *America*—Chicago, Colon, Magellan Straits, Niagara Falls, St. Lawrence River.
   (d) *World*—Bass Straits, Bering Straits, Cook Straits Malacca Straits, Port Said.
2. EITHER Write a short description of a passage through the Panama Canal as if you were a passenger in a ship.
   OR Describe a canal in your district.
3. The Panama Canal has been described as "a water bridge over mountains". With what town do you connect each of the following: (a) Tower Bridge (b) Bridge of Sighs; (c) Golden Gate Bridge; (d) Forth Bridge; (e) Brooklyn Bridge?
4. A ship is raised by locks. For what are the following used: (a) breeches buoy; (b) dumb waiter (c) elevator; (d) escalator; (e) funicular railway?
5. Give a short description of how a ship is raised from one level to another.
6. The mosquito germ was discovered by Sir Ronald Ross. With what medical discoveries are the following people connected: (a) Madame Curie; (b) Alexander Fleming; (c) Louis Pasteur; (d) Röntgen; (e) James Simpson?
7. Canals are used as a means of transport. Name at least four other methods of transporting goods.
8. William Paterson founded the Bank of England. What persons are connected with the founding of: (a) Boy Scouts; (b) Navy; (c) Nursing; (d) Penny Post; (e) Police?

THE CONQUEST OF EVEREST

*This account is adapted from "The Ascent of Everest"
by Colonel John Hunt, the leader of the British
Expedition which conquered Mount Everest.*

THIS is the story of how, on 29th May, 1953, two men reached the top of Everest, the highest mountain in the world.

The height of Everest is 29,002 feet and until 1953, no one had been able to climb much above 28,000 feet, either from the north through Tibet or from the south through Nepal. Indeed, only on about six occasions had it been possible to get within 1,000 feet of the summit. Time after time men had reached this point only to be forced back by bad weather, by misfortune or when they were too weak to tackle those last few hundred feet. Everest, it had been made clear, would not yield its crown easily.

No one can control the weather, and this, together with the lack of oxygen in the air, is the most important obstacle facing climbers on Everest. To counter the ill-effects of the rarefied air, supplies of oxygen can be inhaled by the climber from cylinders carried on his back. When this is breathed in, the climber can move faster and more confidently, though, of course, the weight of the equipment itself is a further strain on the climber's strength.

The chance to get up Everest is limited to May or June or the early part of October, that is, before the monsoon sets in or after it dies away, for all through the winter, a fierce wind, strong and desperately cold, blows from the north-west and no human being could withstand its onslaught.

The approach to Everest is made by way of a valley known as the Western Cwm, which leads to the very foot of the mountain; but to get this far, it is by no means straightforward climbing. Two or three miles

ahead, rising 4,000 feet above the valley lie the icy slopes named the Lhotse Face, which must be scaled to reach the feature known as the South Col, midway between the top of Everest and its nearest neighbour, Lhotse. Between the South Col and the summit of Everest another 3,000 feet remain to be climbed, on slopes exposed to the wind and in an atmosphere in which the climber must rely increasingly on his oxygen equipment for strength and stamina. In preparing for their attack on Everest, members of the 1953 expedition had the advantage of knowing in advance the nature of the perils and hardships that would face their new challenge.

One of the most important tasks was the selection of a party of climbers and, in this matter, four qualifications were necessary, age, temperament, experience and physique. The chosen party, consisting mainly of well-tried British climbers with two from New Zealand, arrived in India by air, sea, rail and ultimately on foot to meet at Kathmandu, the capital city of Nepal, a small kingdom in the Himalayan mountains. Twenty of the best Sherpas were engaged for these sturdy hill-men from eastern Nepal, have all the qualities of born mountaineers. Among them was the renowned "Tiger" Tenzing, who was making his sixth attempt at Everest and who, with the Swiss guide Lambert, had reached the South-East ridge in 1952, only about 1,000 feet from the top.

Thyangboche, which was our base camp, must be one of the most beautiful places in the world. The height is well over 12,000 feet. The monastery buildings stand upon a knoll at the end of a big spur. Surrounded by satellite dwellings, all quaintly constructed and oddly mediaeval in appearance, it provides a grandstand beyond comparison for the finest mountain scenery in the world.

Beyond a foreground of dark firs, lichen-draped birch and rhododendrons, now dwarfed by altitude to bush size, tower immense ice peaks in every quarter, while the Everest group bars the head of the valley. Standing spellbound by this wonderful scenery upon an open grassy alp where yaks grazed peacefully, the party deemed life very good.

From the base camp, rehearsals and practices were carried out and these helped the climbers to get accustomed to their equipment, to become used to the increased heights and to become acquainted with each other. By setting up camps at various levels, the party was able to explore the way ahead and bring up loads of provisions and climbing equipment, thus giving the final

assault on the summit a greater chance of success. After overcoming the difficulties and hazards of the Icefall, the Western Cwm and the Lhotse face, the advance base was set up at the South Col, from which the assault parties were sent out.

Though the first summit attempt by Charles Evans and Tom Bourdillon failed, the second assault team consisting of Edmund Hillary and Sherpa Tenzing set out with full confidence. The conquest of the summit of Everest is told in Hillary's own words.

"The weather for Everest, seemed practically perfect. Insulated as we were in all our down clothing and windproofs, we suffered no discomfort from cold or wind. However, on one occasion I removed my sun-glasses to examine more closely a difficult section of the ridge but was very soon blinded by the fine snow driven by the bitter wind and hastily replaced them. I went on cutting steps. To my surprise, I was enjoying the climb as much as I had ever enjoyed a fine ridge in my own New Zealand Alps.

"After an hour's steady going we reached the foot of the most formidable-looking problem on the ridge— a rock step some forty feet high. We had known of the existence of this step from aerial photographs and had also seen it through our binoculars from Thyangboche. We realised that at this altitude it might well spell the difference between success and failure.

"The rock itself, smooth and almost holdless, might have been an interesting afternoon problem to a group of expert rock climbers in the Lake District, but here it was a barrier beyond our feeble strength to overcome. I could see no way of turning it on the steep rock bluff on the west, but fortunately another possibility of tackling it remained.

"On its east side was another great cornice, and running up the full forty feet of the step was a narrow crack between the cornice and the rock. Leaving Tenzing to belay me as best he could, I jammed my way into this crack; then, kicking backwards with my crampons, I sank their spikes deep into the frozen snow behind me and levered myself off the ground.

"Taking advantage of every little rockhold and all the force of knee, shoulder and arms I could muster, I literally cramponed backwards up the crack, with a fervent prayer that the cornice would remain attached to the rock. Despite the considerable effort involved, my progress although slow was steady, and as Tenzing paid out the rope, I inched my way upwards until I could finally reach over the top of the rock and drag myself out of the crack on to a wide ledge.

"For a few moments I lay regaining my breath and for the first time really felt the fierce determination that nothing now could stop us reaching the top. I took a firm stance on the ledge and signalled to Tenzing to come on up. As I heaved hard on the rope, Tenzing wriggled his way up the crack and finally collapsed exhausted at the top, like a giant fish, when it has just been hauled from the sea after a terrible struggle.

"I checked both our oxygen sets and roughly calculated our flow rates. Everything seemed to be going well. Probably owing to the strain imposed on him by the trouble with his oxygen set, Tenzing had been moving rather slowly; but he was climbing safely and this was the major consideration. His only comment on my enquiring of his condition was to smile and wave along the ridge.

"The ridge continued as before. Giant cornices on the right, steep rock slopes on the left. I went on cutting steps on the narrow strip of snow. The ridge curved away to the right and we had no idea where the top was. As I cut around the back of one hump, another higher one would swing into view. Time was passing and the ridge seemed never-ending.

"In one place where the angle of the ridge had eased off, I tried cramponing without cutting steps, hoping this would save time. But I quickly realised that our margin of safety on these steep slopes at this altitude was too small, so I went on step-cutting.

"I was beginning to tire a little now. I had been cutting steps continuously for two hours, and Tenzing, too, was moving very slowly. As I chipped steps around still another corner, I wondered rather dully just how long we could keep it up.

"Our original zest had now quite gone and it was turning more into a grim struggle. I then realised that the ridge ahead, instead of still monotonously rising, now dropped, sharply away, and far below, I could see the North Col and the Rongbuk Glacier. I look upwards to see a narrow snowy ridge running up to a snow summit. *A few more whacks of the ice-axe in the firm snow and we stood on top.*

"My initial feelings were of relief—relief that there were no more steps to cut—no more ridges to traverse—no more humps to tantalise us with hopes of success. I looked at Tenzing and in spite of the balaclava, goggles and oxygen mask, all encrusted with long icicles that concealed his face, there was no disguising his infectious grin of pure delight as he looked all around him. We shook hands and then Tenzing threw his arms around my shoulders and we thumped each other on the back until we were almost breathless. It was 11.30 a.m. The ridge had taken us two and a half hours, but it seemed like a lifetime.

"I turned off the oxygen and removed my set. I had carried my camera, loaded with colour film, inside my shirt to keep it warm, so I now produced it and got Tensing to pose on top for me, waving his axe on which

was a string of flags—British, Nepalese, United Nations. and Indian. Then I turned my attention to the great stretch of country lying below us in every direction.

"To the east was our giant neighbour Makalu, un-explored and unclimbed. Far away across the clouds, the great bulk of Kangchenjunga loomed on the horizon. To the west, Cho Oyu, our old adversary of 1952, dominated the scene and we could see the great un-explored ranges of Nepal stretching off into the distance.

"Meanwhile, Tenzing had made a little hole in the snow and in it he placed various small articles of food—a bar of chocolate, a packet of biscuits and a handful of lollies. Small offerings, indeed, but at least a token gift to the Gods that all devout Buddhists believe have their home in this lofty summit. On the South Col, two days before, Hunt had given me a small crucifix which he asked me to take to the top. I, too, made a hole in the snow and placed the crucifix beside Tenzing's gifts."

INTERESTING FACTS ON FAMOUS ACHIEVEMENTS

1. What makes men want to climb mountains, risk their lives or suffer voluntary hardships? Rarely is it for personal gain; in the majority of cases, it is to satisfy man's spirit of adventure. Recognition of success is often shown and the climbers *Colonel Hunt* and *Edmund Hillary* were knighted for their brilliant conquest of *Everest*. This mountain belongs to the loftiest range of mountains in the world, the *Himalayas*, a word which means "the abode of snow".

2. Success does not always bring its rewards. *Captain Robert Scott* and his band of courageous men battled their way to the *South Pole* in January 1912, only to find that the Norwegian *Roald Amundsen* had reached the Pole first, just one month before them. While Amundsen's triumph was a truly great one, the epic story of Captain Scott's last expedition is not one of failure, but of dogged British heroism and self-sacrifice which was an example to the world.

3. Another "near miss" was Norwegian *Fridtjof Nansen's* attempt to reach the *North Pole*. By his famous and hazardous voyage in the *"Fram"*, in which he came to a distance 190 miles short of the Pole, he discovered that instead of it being on land, the North Pole is an ice-covered sea. The "Fram" has been preserved in the national museum in Oslo. The first person to reach the North Pole was an American *Robert Peary*, who led a successful expedition in 1909.

4. It was however personal gain that, in the thirteenth century, made the Venetian brothers, *Nicolo* and *Maffeo Polo*, extend their trading posts until they reached *Cathay*, the ancient name for China. These daring merchants wandered across the Mongolian deserts, climbed the mountains of Tibet and found their way to the court of the Emperor of China. They returned with their treasures, and *Marco Polo*, Nicolo's son, gained everlasting fame by writing down his wonderful stories and adventures in the Far East.

5. In the making of great discoveries, sailors have played a large part. Ever since *Columbus* discovered America the quest for new worlds to conquer has inspired many sailors to explore unknown seas. *Vasco da Gama*, a Portuguese sailor made a sea voyage by the Cape of Good Hope to India and *Ferdinand Magellan*, a fellow countryman, had the distinction of being the first man to sail round the world. English sailors, like *Sir Francis Drake*, *Henry Hudson* and *Captain James Cook*, followed their example and made dangerous voyages and interesting discoveries in uncharted seas.

6. The desire to be free to worship God as they pleased, inspired the *Pilgrim Fathers* to seek a home in the New World. Despite the perils of a voyage across the Atlantic, and the hardships of colonising unexplored territory, they settled and prospered in what is now known as the New England States. Two centuries later, a similar pioneering spirit drove the first *covered wagons* to the west and so

opened up for development the great resources of the United States. Among the settlers in South Africa are the *Huguenots* who were driven out of France because of their Protestant religion.

7. The spreading of Christianity has also been responsible for many great deeds of bravery and endurance. The journeys of *Saint Paul*, so remarkably described in the Bible, have lent inspiration to many missionaries who carried the gospel to heathen races. Scotsman *David Livingstone* spent a life-time converting the natives and exploring the unknown territories of darkest Africa. Besides his tremendous work of Christian conversion, he discovered the *Victoria Falls* and the country now known as *Malawi*. He died in Africa, and for his brave deeds and indomitable courage, he was buried in Westminster Abbey. Another famous Scots explorer, *Mungo Park* penetrated the dense jungles of West Africa and, in the cause of progress, followed the unknown course of the river Niger for over a thousand miles.

8. The qualities of bravery and courage are not confined to any single nation for each country has its own list of heroes and daring adventurers. *Jacques Cartier* and later *Samuel Champlain* were two famous Frenchmen, who succeeded in exploring the great *St. Lawrence* estuary of Canada, and in establishing a French colony there. Towards the end of the eighteenth century, amid the dangers of the pathless Rocky Mountains, the Scotsman *Alexander Mackenzie* and the American *Simon Fraser* showed great powers of endurance, in tracing from source to mouth the famous rivers that bear their names.

9. Among those who blazed the trail of modern progress, were two intrepid English airmen, *John Alcock* and *Arthur Brown* who flew the Atlantic for the first time in 1919. They took off in a biplane from St. Johns, Newfoundland, and after a flight, in which they en-

countered heavy gales and storms, they landed in Ireland, having completed in 16 hours the first trans-Atlantic air crossing at an average speed of 118 miles per hour.

10. Sir Edmund Hillary is also associated with the 1957-58 Commonwealth expedition of *crossing the Antarctic continent by land.* From Scott Base in Macmurdo Sound, he travelled over the snow-bound country to the South Pole, where he was joined by the English scientific explorer *Dr. Vivien Fuchs*, who had come from Shackleton Base in Vahsel Bay on the opposite side of the continent. Hillary flew back to his base, but Dr. Fuchs continued his land journey and successfully completed the two thousand mile crossing of this south polar region.

QUESTIONS ON THE STORY

1. Give the date when Mt. Everest was first conquered.
2. What had prevented previous climbers from reaching the top?
3. How did the climbers overcome the thin air which exists at such heights?
4. In what way did this equipment help the climbers?
5. Name three difficult places that had to be scaled before the attack on the summit could be made.
6. What qualities were necessary in the men chosen for this expedition?
7. How did the party arrive at Kathmandu?

8. How many Sherpas were in the party? Name one of them.
9. What kind of buildings were at the base camp at Thyangboche?
10. Name any animal that can be found there.
11. Why were camps set up at various levels on the mountain?
12. From what place was the assault on the summit to be made?
13. Who made the first attempt to reach the top?
14. Tell how Hillary managed to overcome the difficulty of the forty foot rock step.
15. In what way did they manage to climb the topmost ridge?
16. When did Hillary realise that they had reached the summit?
17. What did the climbers do when they reached the top?
18. What flags had Tenzing on his ice-axes, when he was photographed on the summit of Everest?
19. What did the climbers leave on the summit?
20. Why did they leave them?

QUESTIONS ON THE INTERESTING FACTS

1. (a) What does "Himalaya" mean?
   (b) What award did Hunt and Hillary receive?
2. (a) Who first reached the South Pole?
   (b) Name another explorer who reached it shortly afterwards.
3. (a) What did Nansen discover about the North Pole?
   (b) What has happened to Nansen's ship?
   (c) Who reached the North Pole first?

4. (*a*) What was the ancient name for China?
   (*b*) Why was Marco Polo famous?
5. (*a*) Name two Portuguese sailors who discovered new sea routes.
   (*b*) Name two famous English navigators.
6. (*a*) Why did the Pilgrim Fathers go to the New World?
   (*b*) What mode of travel was used by the first travellers across America?
7. (*a*) Name the colony founded by David Livingstone.
   (*b*) What journey of exploration was made by Mungo Park?
8. (*a*) Who were the first explorers of the St. Lawrence river?
   (*b*) Name two other Canadian explorers.
9. (*a*) How long did the first trans-Atlantic flight take?
   (*b*) Where did the fliers take off and where did they land?
10. (*a*) How did Sir Edmund Hillary and Dr. Fuchs tackle the crossing of the south polar continent?
    (*b*) What distance approximately was covered by each explorer?

DEVELOPMENT EXERCISES

1. Point out on the map of the world.
   (*a*) India, the Himalayas, Everest, Tibet, Nepal.
   (*b*) Africa, Cape of Good Hope, Victoria Falls, Malawi, River Niger.
   (*c*) Canada, Rocky Mountains, St. Lawrence River, Fraser River, Mackenzie River.
2. EITHER (*a*) Write a short account of any great achievement in the twentieth century.
   OR (*b*) If you could have been a famous explorer, which one would you have been? Give your reasons.

3. The conquest of Everest is regarded as an epic story of endurance. Give an example of each of the following: (*a*) a romantic story; (*b*) a sea story; (*c*) a war story; (*d*) a detective story; (*e*) a ghost story.

4. Everest is in Nepal. In what countries are the following peaks: (*a*) Ben Nevis; (*b*) Fujiyama; (*c*) Popocatepetl; (*d*) Kilimanjaro; (*e*) the Matterhorn?

5. Many people are killed each year in climbing accidents. Give a few safety hints you would recommend for climbers.

6. Nansen's famous ship was the *"Fram"*. With whom are the following ships connected (*a*) *Discovery*; (*b*) *Golden Hind*; (*c*) *Mayflower*; (*d*) *Santa Maria*; (*e*) *Victory*?

7. Everest is the highest mountain in the world. Name (*a*) the highest building; (*b*) the largest city; (*c*) the longest river; (*d*) the biggest ship; (*e*) the largest ocean, in the world.

8. Make a list of explorers, giving name, native country and achievement, e.g. Amundsen—Norway—he was the first man to reach the South Pole.

THE YOUNG POET

*In the following extract from " Young Walter Scott "
by E. J. Gray the young budding writer, still a
schoolboy, receives some encouragement from the
reception given his very first lines of verse.*

WALTER LIMPED to his place in the Rector's
class and sat down. He was ninth. There were
one hundred and seven boys behind him. He did not
know just how it had happened, but Latin as Dr. Adam
taught it seemed to be easier and more interesting, and
he had mounted to the first form almost before he knew
where he was. Now that he was here he was going to
take good care to stay. He had a reputation to maintain
now. The Rector had said of him, " Many of the lads
understand the *Latin* better, but Gualterus Scott is
behind few in following and enjoying the author's
meaning."

James Buchan was *dux*. He had kept first place ever
since Wattie had been coming to the High School. No
use trying to dislodge him. Ninth was good enough.
Ninth, or maybe eighth.

Dr. Adam came in with his gown billowing out
behind him, his cheeks red and his hair slightly ruffled
by the wind, and sat down at his desk on the platform.
For a moment his thin fine hands were busy among his
papers and piles of books, then he looked up and gazed
out lovingly over his flock.

Walter's breath quickened, he felt the class behind him stir attentively. To-day was the day.

"Yes," pronounced the Rector, "I have read your verses, the verses of those of you who were interested enough to make this additional effort. I think you will find when you grow older that no effort which you put into your school work ever fails to bear fruit far beyond the due and fit but still limited rewards of the classroom. I have been teaching boys since I was a young man of nineteen and I am acquainted with the subsequent history of every lad who has passed under my control, and I say to you that I could have prophesied in advance what their several fates would be, for invariably those who were diligent in school have prospered in after life and those who were idle and inattentive in their lessons have failed signally in the greater tasks of life."

The good doctor was off on his hobbyhorse. He would go on until he felt the attention of the lads slacken and then he would switch abruptly back to the matter in hand. His wise grey eyes with the twinkle at the corners saw every shade of expression that passed over their faces.

"I have read your papers carefully, in which you have turned passages of Virgil into English verse, and I have chosen two, one to receive the prize and one to receive honourable mention.

Now was the moment.

"The prize is awarded to Colin Mackenzie for Dido's speech. After I have read the piece, the author of it will please step forward to the platform."

He read the poem carefully, with the kinds of emphasis necessary to make the metre come out right, and Walter said to himself thoughtfully that it was very fine indeed. He wouldn't have thought old Colin had it in him.

He looked very handsome when he went up to receive his prize, which all, craning their necks, perceived at once to be nothing but a calendar. His face, pale from

excitement, was in striking contrast to his dark eyes and dark hair; he was tall and slender and even in his school clothes he had a look of elegance.

As he climbed over Wattie to get back to his place, Walter gave him a congratulatory thump on the shoulder.

The Rector picked up another sheet of paper.

" Gualterus Scott receives honourable mention for a description of Mount Etna:

" In awful ruins Etna thunders high,
    And sends in pitchy whirlwinds to the sky
    Black clouds of smoke. . . ."

Wattie felt silly, sitting there while his poem was being read out. His face flamed and his fingers were damp in his pockets. And yet, deep in his heart was a solid core of contentment. Never before had anything sounded quite so good in his ears.

" The stones made liquid as the huge mass flies,
    (The end was almost reached now)
    Then back again with greater weight recoils
    While Etna thundering from the bottom boils."

He limped forward and received his paper and a handshake from the Rector. The class clapped and stamped—more, he felt, because they seized any excuse for making a racket than because they wished to pay honest tribute to literary achievement—until they were firmly ordered to cease.

He presented the poem to his mother that evening. After she had read it over twice and commented on its merits, she wrote on it " My Walter's first lines, 1782," and put it away carefully in a drawer in her bureau.

" Why'd you write that ? " he asked curiously.

" Because I think they'll not be your last. These were a translation. One of these days you'll be writing something out of your own head."

INTERESTING FACTS ON SIR WALTER SCOTT

1. Scotland, despite its small size on the map, can boast of two writers whose works are still known and read all over the world—Robert Burns, and Sir Walter Scott. Scott was born in *Edinburgh* in 1771, although his ancestors hailed from the Borders, the region with which we usually associate him. While a baby, young Walter suffered a severe bout of infantile paralysis which left his right leg partially lame for the rest of his life. From an early age Scott was deeply fascinated by the *past*; by tales of feuds and battles, knights in shining armour and ladies in distress, by the Jacobite Rebellions and by Bonnie Prince Charlie.

2. After a period at the ancient High School of Edinburgh Scott entered college to study Law, and, in the summer of 1792, he passed his final examinations to qualify as an *advocate*. By this time Scott's learning was tremendous: he had read everything of note in English literature, while he also read easily in French, German, Spanish and Italian. Latin he also knew soundly, though it was always a source of regret to him that he never took up Greek. As well as book learning, however, Scott liked to see things for himself, and each year he would explore the countryside, if not in the Borders, in the Highlands. He would mix with the common people there who could tell him tales of long ago, and recite to him the old traditional *ballads* which he collected and later published.

3. Not satisfied, however, with merely writing down other people's poetry Scott set out to compose his own; before long he had won a great reputation as a narrative poet all over the British Isles. He was introduced to Robert Burns, was entertained by King George IV, and was actually asked if he would become Poet Laureate. He refused this high honour, however, and the English poet *Robert Southey* was appointed instead. By 1811, Scott was making by his poetry over £1,000 a year, a very great income in these days. His poems are long but full of action and very exciting, the most famous being "The Lay of the Last Minstrel", "Marmion", and "The Lady of the Lake".

4. In 1811, Scott, now enjoying great fame and wealth, paid out the colossal sum of £4,000 for a piece of land near Melrose, beautifully situated, on which he intended to build a new home. *Abbotsford*, as he called it, is still a fascinating place to visit. The great house, which replaced the older farm-house, was begun in 1822 and represents all Scott lived for. It is a real treasure-chest of the past, containing such things as the Wallace chair, made from wood taken from the house in which the great Scottish patriot Sir William Wallace was betrayed, Bonnie Prince Charlie's drinking cup as well as a lock of his hair, Napoleon's pistols, the swords of Rob Roy the Highland outlaw and of the famous Marquis of Montrose, Burns' tumbler and a writing desk made from pieces of wood from the ships of the Spanish Armada.

5. In due course Scott turned to writing *historical novels*, a task for which he was especially suited. First, he had this intense interest in the past which was allied with great learning. Secondly, he possessed a great and human understanding of people. For this last gift his training as an advocate and subsequent experience in court, where he came into contact with all sorts of memorable characters, were partly responsible. The years that followed saw some truly great novels flow from his pen, beginning with "Waverley" (1814), an exciting story of the 'Forty-five rebellion and Bonnie Prince Charlie. At first, Scott was content to leave these novels unsigned, but, before long, people realised only he could have been the author.

6. "*The Waverley Novels*", as they are called, are among the most famous works in prose in the whole field of English literature. "Waverley" itself was followed in turn by "Guy Mannering" (1815), "The Antiquary" (1816), "Old Mortality" (1816), "Rob Roy" (1818), "The Heart of Midlothian" (1818), and "Ivanhoe" (1820). One great book followed another, and Scott was now at the height of his reputation; indeed, he was made a baronet in 1818. These novels are distinguished first and foremost by the *unforgettable characters* they contain, such as the ruthless Balfour of Burley in "Old Mortality" and the demented, wild-eyed "Meg Merrilees" of "Guy Mannering". Scott's power of *vivid description* is another great quality; scenes such as the marshalling of the two armies at the Battle of Bothwell Bridge or the storming of the castle in "Ivanhoe" are breathtaking in their descriptiveness.

7. Sir Walter, as he became, was always very interested in animals, especially *dogs*. He writes that he found his dogs—Maida, a big deerhound, Hamlet, a black greyhound, and the dandies, Pepper, Mustard and Ketchup—a great source of comfort to him during a hard day's work. He would pause for a while in the middle of a sentence, lay down his pen and pat them fondly as they lay about his feet. Of course, they also accompanied him as he walked slowly along the banks of the Tweed or in the shadow of the Eildon Hills. In Abbotsford to this day a beautiful painting of Scott with *Maida* beside him by the famous artist Sir Henry Raeburn hangs on the wall of the drawing-room.

8. Many of Scott's most famous novels were written in great bodily pain, a sickness which afflicted him increasingly from 1817 onward. Many a lesser man would have given in to this, but showing great spirit, Sir Walter struggled on. An even greater disaster, however, occurred in 1826 when Scott's publisher, the firm of *James Ballantyne*, went bankrupt to the extent of over £250,000, and Scott himself was almost ruined. It was then that he wrote the famous sentence "*My own right hand shall pay my debt*," meaning that he would write on until he had paid back all he felt he owed. A further misfortune was the death of his wife the same year. Despite all these tremendous shocks, Scott's courage triumphed in the end, for, with such books as "Woodstock", "The Fair Maid of Perth", the popular "Tales of a Grandfather", and "Anne of Geierstein" all his debts were, by the time of his death, successfully paid.

9. Sad to relate, however, Scott, in struggling to pay off his debts, literally worked himself to death; but not before this picture of the great man bravely fighting against hard times had caught hold of the imagination of the general public. So much so that when the government heard of Sir Walter's plans to spend the winter of 1831 abroad in a last desperate attempt to improve his health, they put a frigate of the Royal Navy at his disposal. The journey ended, however, with a rapid worsening of Scott's condition. The whole country prayed for his recovery, but he knew within himself that he was dying and longed to get home to Abbotsford. Built into the wall that flanks the road from Galashiels to Melrose there is a *small plaque* which records that it was at that point Sir Walter halted the carriage to gaze for the very last time down his beloved valley of the Tweed.

10. Sir Walter Scott died on September 21st, 1832, and was buried in the ruined *Abbey of Dryburgh*. If you go to see his grave to-day you will probably be struck by the peaceful beauty around and also by the fact that this ancient abbey is indeed a fitting last resting place since it breathes an atmosphere of the past, just such an atmosphere as this "*Wizard of the North*" came to cherish so fondly.

QUESTIONS ON THE STORY

1. What was Walter's place in class?
2. To what did he attribute his improvement?
3. How did the Rector describe Walter's knowledge of Latin?
4. Who was dux?
5. Was the verse competition compulsory?
6. At what age did Dr. Adam begin teaching?
7. In what way could he forecast how his pupils would fare when they left school?
8. Who was the Latin author to be translated?
9. One was to receive a prize; what was the other to receive?
10. Who won the prize?

11. What passage had the winner translated?
12. Describe how the Rector read the winning poem.
13. What was presented as first prize?
14. What was the contrast in the winner's appearance that struck Walter?
15. What was the subject of Walter's poem?
16. What was the main reason for the class making a noise?
17. How many times did Walter's mother read his poem?
18. In what year was the poem written?
19. Where did Mrs. Scott put the poem?
20. What did she forecast?

QUESTIONS ON THE INTERESTING FACTS

1. Name two major Scottish writers.
2. What was the profession Scott chose to follow?
3. (*a*) Name three honours that came Scott's way.
   (*b*) Who was appointed Poet Laureate instead of Scott?
   (*c*) Name three of Scott's narrative poems.
4. Near what Border town is Abbotsford situated?
5. What objects of historical interest can be seen there?
6. Give two reasons for Scott eventually turning to historical novels and for his great success in that field.
7. (*a*) What was the name given to his first great novel?
   (*b*) Give one reason why Scott's novels are so famous.
   (*c*) Name one of his famous characters.
8. (*a*) What breed of dog was Maida?
   (*b*) Who painted the great picture of Scott and Maida?
   (*c*) Where can this be seen to-day?

9. Describe briefly each of the three misfortunes which befell Sir Walter from 1817 to his death.
10. (*a*) In what way did the government show great respect for Scott?
    (*b*) What occasion does the wall-plaque record?
    (*c*) Where is Sir Walter Scott buried?

DEVELOPMENT EXERCISES

1. Burns is regarded as *the* great Scottish poet, Scott as *the* great Scottish novelist. Find out where Burns was born. Limiting your answer to the *lives* of the men themselves, what strikes you as a great difference between the two writers?
2. What counties make up the region of Scotland called "the Borders"?
3. Give the names of *two* English ballads and *two* Scottish ones.
4. Scott refused to accept the position of Poet Laureate. Who is the present Poet Laureate?
5. Abbotsford is the house associated with Sir Walter Scott. What famous people are associated with the following buildings?—(*a*) 10 Downing Street; (*b*) The White House; (*c*) No. 221B Baker Street; (*d*) Chartwell; (*e*) Sandringham.
6. Who was the commander of the English fleet which defeated the Spanish Armada?
7. "Old Mortality" is a story about the Covenanters. Who were the Covenanters?
8. Meg Merrilees is one of Scott's most famous characters. Who created the following characters?—(*a*) Fagin; (*b*) Gulliver; (*c*) Macbeth; (*d*) Peter Pan; (*e*) Huckleberry Finn.

THE COMBAT

IT had been agreed, on account of the heat of the climate, that the contest, which was the cause of the present assemblage of various nations at the Diamond of the Desert, should take place at one hour after sunrise. The wide lists, which had been constructed under the inspection of the Knight of the Leopard, enclosed a space of hard sand, which was one hundred and twenty yards long by forty in width. They extended in length from north to south, so as to give both parties the equal advantage of the rising sun.

Saladin's royal seat was erected on the western side of the enclosure, just in the centre, where the combatants were expected to meet in mid encounter. Opposed to this was a gallery with closed casements, so contrived that the ladies, for whose accommodation it was erected, might see the fight without being themselves exposed to view. Thrones had also been erected, but the Archduke of Austria, perceiving that his was lower than King Richard's, refused to occupy it; and Coeur de Lion, who would have submitted to much ere any formality should have interfered with the combat, readily agreed that the sponsors, as they were called, should remain on horseback during the fight.

Soon the noise of timbrels was heard, at the sound of which the whole of the Saracen cavaliers threw themselves from their horses, and prostrated themselves, as if for a second morning prayer. This was to give an opportunity to the Queen, with Edith and her attendants, to pass from the pavilion to the gallery intended for them. Fifty of Saladin's guards, escorted them with naked sabres, whose orders were to cut to pieces, whomsoever, were he prince or peasant, should venture to gaze on the ladies as they passed, or even to presume to raise his head until the cessation of the music should make all men aware that they were lodged in their gallery, not to be gazed on by the curious eye.

This superstitious observance of Oriental reverence to the fair sex called forth from Queen Berengaria some criticisms very unfavourable to Saladin and his country; but their den, being securely closed and guarded by their attendants, she was under the necessity of contenting herself with seeing, and laying aside for the present the still more exquisite pleasure of being seen.

The trumpets of the challenger then rung a flourish, and a herald-at-arms proclaimed at the eastern end of the lists: "Here stands a good knight, Sir Kenneth of Scotland, champion for the royal King Richard of England, who accuseth Conrade, Marquis of Montserrat, of foul treason and dishonour done to the said King."

The esquires of the combatants now approached, and delivered to each his shield and lance, assisting to hang the former around his neck, that his two hands might remain free, one for the management of the bridle, the other to direct the lance. The shield of the Scot displayed the leopard while the shield of the Marquis bore, in reference to his title, a serrated and rocky mountain. Each shook his lance aloft, as if to ascertain the weight and toughness of the unwieldy weapon, and then laid it in the rest. The sponsors, heralds, and squires now retired to the barriers, and the combatants sat opposite to each other, face to face, with couched lance and closed visor, the human form so completely enclosed, that they looked more like statues of molten iron than beings of flesh and blood.

They stood thus for perhaps three minutes, when, at a
signal given by Saladin, a hundred instruments rent the
air with their brazen clamours, and each champion
striking his horse with the spurs, and slacking the rein,
the horses started into full gallop, and the knights met
in mid-space with a shock like a thunderbolt. The
victory was not in doubt—no, not one moment. Conrade
indeed, showed himself a practised warrior; for he
struck his antagonist knightly in the middle of the shield,
bearing his lance so straight and true that it shivered
into splinters from the steel spear-head up to the very
gauntlet. The horse of Sir Kenneth recoiled two or
three yards and fell on his haunches; but the rider easily
raised him with hand and rein. For Conrade there was no
recovery. Sir Kenneth's lance had pierced through the
shield, through a plated corslet of Milan steel, through a
"secret," or coat of linked mail, worn beneath the corslet,
had wounded him deep in the bosom, and born him
from his saddle, leaving the truncheon of the lance
fixed in the wound.

The sponsors, heralds, and Saladin himself, descending from his throne, crowded around the wounded man, while Sir Kenneth, who had drawn his sword ere yet he discovered his antagonist was totally helpless, now commanded him to avow his guilt. The helmet was hastily unclosed, and the wounded man, gazing wildly on the skies, replied, "What would you more? God hath decided justly—I am guilty; but there are worse traitors in the camp than I. In pity to my soul, let me have a confessor!"

He revived as he uttered these words.

"The talisman—the powerful remedy, royal brother!" said King Richard to Saladin.

"The traitor," answered Saladin, "is more fit to be dragged from the lists to the gallows by the heels, than to profit by its virtues. Nevertheless my royal brother's wish shall be obeyed. Slaves, bear this wounded man to our tent."

"Do not so," said the Templar, who had hitherto stood gloomily looking on in silence. "The royal Duke of Austria and myself will not permit this unhappy Christian prince to be delivered over to the Saracens, that they may try their spells upon him. We are his sponsors, and demand that he be assigned to our care."

"That is, you refuse the certain means offered to recover him?" said Richard.

"Not so," said the Grand Master, recollecting himself. "Saladin useth lawful medicines, he may attend the patient in my tent."

"Do so, I pray thee, good brother," said Richard to Saladin, "though the permission be ungraciously yielded. But now to a more glorious work. Sound, trumpets— shout, England—in honour of England's champion!"

Drum, clarion, trumpet and cymbal rang forth at once, and the deep and regular shout which for ages has been the English acclamation, sounded amidst the shrill and irregular yells of the Arabs, like the diapason of the organ amid the howling of a storm. There was silence at length.

"Brave Knight of the Leopard," resumed Coeur de Lion, "thou hast shown that the Ethiopian may change his skin and the leopard his spots, though clerks quote Scripture for the impossibility. Yet I have more to say to you when I have conducted you to the presence of the ladies, the best judges, and best rewarders, of deeds of chivalry. Come, we will to the pavilion, and lead our conqueror thither in triumph."

Blondel tuned his harp to its boldest measure, to welcome the introduction of the victor into the pavilion of Queen Berengaria. He entered, supported on either side by his sponsors, and knelt gracefully down before the Queen, though more than half the homage was silently rendered to Edith, who sat on her right hand.

"And what expect you from beneath this iron shell?" said Richard, as the removal of the casque gave to view the noble countenance of Sir Kenneth, his face glowing with recent exertion, and not less so with present emotion. "What think ye of him, gallants and beauties?" said Richard. "Here terminate his various disguises. He hath knelt before you unknown, save by his worth; he arises, equally distinguished by birth and by fortune. The adventurous knight, Kenneth, arises David, Earl of Huntingdon, Prince Royal of Scotland!"

There was a general exclamation of surprise and the King continued, "We Plantagenets boast soft and feeling hearts, Edith," turning to his cousin with an expression which called the blood into her cheek. "Give me thy hand, my fair cousin, and, Prince of Scotland, thine."

The next day saw Richard's return to his own camp and in a short space afterwards the young Earl of Huntingdon was espoused by Edith Plantagenet. Saladin sent as a nuptial present on this occasion, the celebrated talisman. Though many cures were wrought by it in Europe, none equalled in success and celebrity those which Saladin achieved. It is still in existence, having been bequeathed by the Earl of Huntingdon to a brave Knight of Scotland, Sir Simon of the Lee, in whose ancient and highly honoured family it is still preserved. From Sir Walter Scott's *"Talisman"*. (ADAPTED)

INTERESTING FACTS ABOUT THE CRUSADES

1. Long ago pilgrims made journeys to the Holy Sepulchre in Jerusalem. *The Saracens*, a name given to Arabs and Turks who worshipped the prophet Mohammed, had conquered the country and wrecked the Holy City, killing all the Christians there. The *Crusades* or wars of the Cross were formed by Christians from all over Europe to drive these fierce Muslims from the Holy Land. The Saracen was known by his *crescent* standard, while the badge of the Crusader was a *cross*.

2. The pilgrims, who had visited the Holy Land and returned to their own countries, carried a palm cross in their hats and were known as *Palmers*. As they had wonderful tales to tell of the countries they had seen, they were always welcomed. Beggars often took advantage of this, and, by the simple ruse of carrying palm crosses and inventing weird stories, they were accepted as palmers and given generous hospitality. The effigies on tombstones give a clue to the part played by nobles in the Crusades. If the legs of the carved figure are crossed, then he went on Crusade and returned, but if the feet rest on a lion, then he died on Crusade.

3. The First Crusade was started by a French monk, *Peter the Hermit*, who preached about the dreadful experiences he had on a pilgrimage to the Holy Land. His fiery preaching stirred people from many countries to flock to the banner of the cross. In the two hundred years after the First Crusade of 1094, there were altogether eight crusades. Although in the first one the Crusaders managed to capture Jerusalem, all the other expeditions were failures. One of the most tragic was the *Children's Crusade*, when children from many lands gathered to go and plead the Christian cause with the Turks. They only managed to reach the Mediterranean ports, whence they were shipped abroad and sold as slaves by wicked traders.

4. One of the greatest Saracen rulers was *Saladin* who opposed Richard I, or Richard Coeur de Lion (the "Lion Heart") in the Third Crusade. Saladin was noted as a fair opponent and a man of his word, who was as courteous as a Christian knight. His soldiers, riding swift ponies, were more accustomed to the Holy Land than the heavily armoured Christians who found fighting in such a hot country very difficult. This Crusade failed because the leaders quarrelled among themselves, but Richard came to an agreement with Saladin, whereby pilgrims were allowed to visit the Holy City.

5. *The Knights of St. John* were a sect of monks who had a guest house in Jerusalem, where pilgrims could receive hospitality. While the city was under siege in the First Crusade, they devoted themselves to the care of the sick and wounded. They wore a black robe with a white cross of eight points on it. A remnant of this order can still be seen in the St. John's Ambulance Association, dedicated to the care of the sick. The *Knights Templar* formed another order of military monks, whose headquarters were near the Temple in Jerusalem. They wore red cloaks with a white cross and their duties were to defend the Holy Sepulchre and protect pilgrims. The district of London called Temple is said to have belonged to the Knights Templar.

6. The cruelties of the Crusades gave birth to a new spirit in Europe, making men eager to help the weak and oppressed. This idea of chivalry became part of the rules of knightly conduct. Originally *a knight* was a soldier of birth, who fought bravely and fairly and who was made a knight by one who already belonged to the order of knighthood. His duties were to serve God and his king, to exercise himself in arms, to be loyal and gentle, to protect the weak and to fight to the death for a good cause. In modern times, the order of knighthood is conferred on a person for meritorious service by royalty and allows him to prefix his name, "*Sir*". At the ceremony or *investiture*, the person who is kneeling is dubbed a knight when the monarch touches him on the shoulders with the blade of a sword.

7. The Crusaders brought home many exciting new things. Not only were *carpets*, *silk*, *muslin* and *cotton* materials introduced, but also mulberry trees, on whose leaves silkworms feed to produce *silk*. The silk industry is especially prominent in France. *Tea* and *rice* were brought to Europe for the first time and people learned to flavour their food with the delicious *spices* from the East. The Arabs were clever physicians and astronomers and it was at this time also that the Western people gave up the system of Roman figures in favour of Arabic numerals.

8. When nobles returned from Crusades, they needed money and so they sold land and freedom to peasants who had worked hard and become rich. As well as becoming large farmers, some of these free men became merchants and craftsmen. In the towns they formed corporations or *guilds* which were granted charters of rights by the king. This was the origin of town councils and merchant guilds.

9. The land voyage to Palestine was too long and too dangerous with the result that Crusaders went to *Genoa* or *Venice*, where they embarked in ships for the East. The owners of the vessels made a very profitable business out of transporting the Crusaders, who had to pay heavy charges. These Italian cities ultimately contributed to the failure of the Crusades by refusing to take Crusaders, for they found that they could grow richer by trading with the Saracens than by helping to fight them.

10. The Holy Land, or Palestine, remained firmly in Turkish hands until 1917, when, in the First World War, it was conquered by British forces under General Allenby. It was established as the republic of Israel in 1948 and became the home for the Jewish people.

QUESTIONS ON THE STORY

1. Where did the contest take place?
2. How many yards formed the perimeter of the arena?
3. Why was the length of the arena running from North to South?
4. On what side of the enclosed space were the ladies seated?
5. Why were the casements round the ladies' pavilion closed?
6. Why did the Archduke of Austria refuse to occupy his throne?
7. What agreement was reached by the Archduke and King Richard?
8. What did the Saracens do when the ladies passed to the pavilion?
9. Why did Queen Berengaria not like this Eastern custom?
10. Who were the combatants?
11. What crests were displayed on the shields of the combatants?
12. Who gave the signal for the contest to start?
13. Describe the actual fight.
14. What remedy did King Richard suggest for the wounded Conrade?
15. Who tried to prevent Conrade from being treated by Saladin?
16. Where was the victor taken?
17. Who was the Knight of the Leopard?
18. Who married the victorious knight?
19. What was the Saladin's wedding present?
20. According to the story in whose possession is the talisman now?

QUESTIONS ON THE INTERESTING FACTS

1. (*a*) Give a name to the followers of Mohammed.
   (*b*) Why were the Crusades formed?
2. (*a*) Who were the Palmers?
   (*b*) What trick did beggars use to obtain hospitality?
   (*c*) In what manner is the part played by nobles in the Crusades shown on tombstones?
3. (*a*) How many Crusades were there altogether?
   (*b*) What happened to the children who went on Crusade?
4. (*a*) For what was Saladin renowned?
   (*b*) What great advantage had the Arab soldiers over the Crusaders?
   (*c*) Why did the Third Crusade fail?
5. (*a*) Explain the differences between the Knights of St. John and the Knights Templar.
   (*b*) How did the Temple district of London get its name?
6. (*a*) What were the duties of a knight?
   (*b*) For what is a person awarded a knighthood in modern times?
7. (*a*) Name two things brought from the East by Crusaders.
   (*b*) What system of numbers was used before Arab numerals were introduced?
8. Tell how the merchant guilds originated.
9. (*a*) Name two Italian seaports that benefited from the Crusades.
   (*b*) In what way did these two cities contribute to the failure of the Crusades?
10. (*a*) Who finally conquered the Holy Land?
    (*b*) When was the republic of Israel created?
    (*c*) What race now occupies the Holy Land?

DEVELOPMENT EXERCISES

1. On the map of Europe:
   (a) Point out, Palestine, Jerusalem, Genoa and Venice.
   (b) Trace the route followed by pilgrims from England.
   (c) Name some of the difficulties likely to have been encountered by pilgrims to the Holy Land.

2. EITHER Describe a knight in as much detail as you can.

   OR Write a short account of a pilgrimage as told by a pilgrim.

3. The Cross was the badge of the Crusaders. With what country do you associate the following symbols: (a) Crescent; (b) Hammer and Sickle; (c) Rising Sun; (d) Stars and Stripes; (e) Swastika?

4. Give a brief commentary, in modern radio style, of the combat between Sir Kenneth and Conrade.

5. Damask is material that was connected with the town of Damascus. With what places are the following materials connected: (a) calico; (b) cambric; (c) cashmere; (d) shantung; (e) worsted?

6. The Arab stallion was the fore-runner of the modern racehorse. With what domestic animals are the following places connected: (a) Guernsey; (b) Persia; (c) Rhode Island; (d) Shetland; (e) Skye?

7. The Trade Guilds were composed of the various crafts and trades and many surnames originated from the person's trade, e.g. Adam the Baker became Adam Baker. Compile at list of surnames that were made in this way.

8. (a) A knight has a title "Sir" before his name. What form of address would you use to the following people: (i) a king; (ii) a governor-

general; (iii) the Pope; (iv) A high court judge; (v) the Archbishop of Canterbury?

(b) The wife of a knight is a "Lady". What title is given to the wife of the following: (i) an earl; (ii) a marquis; (iii) a baron; (iv) a duke; (v) an emperor?

9. The combat was fought in an arena. What contests take place on (a) a pitch; (b) a ring; (c) a court; (d) a track; (e) a course?

10. Palmers carried a palm cross. With whom do you associate each of the following: (a) a baton; (b) a crook; (c) a crosier; (d) a crop; (e) a wand?

THE RED CROSS

The greatest movement in the world for the relief of suffering was founded by a Swiss business man named Henri Dunant. He was the eldest child of a well-to-do family, his father being an established merchant of Geneva and a prominent man in the affairs of the town. When he left school, his father apprenticed him to a bank and before long he was sent to the overseas branch in Algeria.

SHORTLY after this, he left the bank to start a business of his own and sought to obtain concessions from the French Emperor Napoleon III. The Emperor, however, was in Italy engaged in a war to free the Italians from Austrian rule. The French had won a battle at Magenta in Northern Italy, but the two armies re-formed and met again, just outside the little village of Solferino. This was in June 1859. Dunant did not manage to see the Emperor. Instead he witnessed the fiercest battle of the century, which resulted in 40,000 dead or wounded. Dunant found himself in the midst of all the horrors of war, hearing the anguished cries of the untended wounded calling for water, a priest or a bullet to end their suffering.

Overwhelmed by the sight of such tragedy, Dunant organised help in the neighbouring town of Castiglione, where many of the wounded had been brought and were lying on straw in the streets, even though churches, schools and every available building had been turned into temporary hospitals. With the help of the women of Castiglione, Dunant made bandages and dressings and brought food and water to the wounded and helped the surgeons to tend them.

The townspeople used what little they had, tearing up their household linen for urgently needed bandages. Dunant himself worked night and day, bringing hope to the wounded and comfort to the dying. As he moved

amongst them in his white tropical clothes, the soldiers called him "The Man in White".

Everyone helped, women of the nobility, tourists and peasants working side by side, giving aid to friend and foe alike, learning by Dunant's example that for those who are suffering there are no barriers and that "All men are brothers". The gentleness and kindness shown by the women helped to revive a little courage and hope in the patients. Even the children lent willing hands and boys and girls ran backwards and forwards fetching water from the public fountain.

Dunant went to the French army commanders and persuaded them to release captured Austrian doctors to help with the many casualties. Before long all the victims were receiving treatment for their wounds.

Worn out and weary with his tremendous efforts, Dunant forgot about his Algerian schemes and went home to Geneva with a burning desire to do what he could to relieve suffering. Three years later, in 1862 he wrote a book called "A Memory of Solferino", in which his vision of the Red Cross took shape and in which he pleaded for voluntary aid societies to be formed in every country, ready and trained for service in time of war. The members of a Swiss Welfare Society formed a committee of five to discuss the ideas in his book.

Dunant's book was read in many countries and his ideas were brought to the notice of the world at large when the committee of five in Geneva called an International Conference. Representatives from fourteen countries, including Great Britain, were present and when they returned they took back with them four proposals, viz:

(a) The formation in each country of what later became known as National Red Cross Societies.

(b) The holding of International Red Cross Conferences.

(c) The establishment on a permanent basis of the Committee of Five who, later, assumed the name of the "International Committee of the Red Cross".

(d) That nations at war should proclaim the neutrality of ambulances and military hospitals, those attending to the wounded, and the wounded themselves; and that a uniform distinctive sign be recognised for the Army Medical Services and for ambulances and hospitals.

The following year, in 1864, the Swiss Government invited Government Representatives to a Conference in Geneva at which an international treaty—The Convention of Geneva—was drawn up to give effect to the fourth proposal. The Red Cross on a white ground—obtained

by reversing the colours of the Swiss flag—was adopted as the symbol of protection. The Red Crescent on a white ground (in the case of Iran, the Red Lion and Sun) is now also the recognised symbol for certain countries.

Later Conventions extended protection to sailors and prisoners of war and in 1949 the Conventions were revised and brought up to date and another clause was added which contained certain measures for the protection of civilians in war time. The four Conventions have now been adopted by most nations in the world.

The International Red Cross movement originating from the first three proposals of the 1863 Conference is now supported by more than 85 countries each having its own National Society which trains its members in nursing, first aid and many branches of welfare and relief work. These societies assist the sick and injured and victims of war, accidents, floods or earthquakes. Any major calamity may bring distress in its wake and the swift help from the Red Cross either in the form of relief supplies or personnel is readily available and contributes to the lessening of human suffering.

Among the important services carried out by the Red Cross in time of war is the tracing of wounded and missing men, maintaining contact with the captured men in prisoner-of-war camps and forwarding to them much needed parcels of food and other necessities. In the last war, a Red Cross postal message scheme for civilians who were separated from their families was established.

Dunant played the part of friend and helper to the wounded from Solferino for only a few weeks, but it was long enough for him to become the hero of one of the most remarkable stories of all time. The Red Cross has grown into a great force to relieve suffering and bring better understanding between the peoples of the world by encouraging them to help one another in time of disaster and need.

INTERESTING FACTS ABOUT THE
RED CROSS

1. When Mrs. Eleanor MacKinnon formed her Red
Cross circles among the school children of Sydney,
Australia, in 1914, she little realised that they were to be
the start of the Junior Red Cross movement. About the
same time Red Cross groups were formed in Schools in
Canada. The idea spread from country to country and
today throughout the world over 55 million boys and
girls are members of the Junior Red Cross.

2. Before the Junior Red Cross sections had been
created, children had played a part in Red Cross relief
work on many occasions. An outstanding example in
the U.S.A. was when they sent materials to give much
needed relief to San Francisco, after the earthquake
which destroyed the city in 1906.

3. The three aims of the Junior Red Cross are: The
Protection of Life and Health; Service to the Sick and
Suffering; and International Friendship and Under-
standing. Its motto is: "Serve one Another".

4. The British Junior Red Cross was officially recognised in 1924 and now has well over 113,000 members.
Of these, 50,721 are in England and Wales, 29,414 in Scotland and the rest in Northern Ireland, the Isle of Man and
in the 41 Overseas Branches of the British Red Cross
Society.

5. Boys and girls, aged 5 to school leaving age, who
belong to the British Junior Red Cross can learn first

aid, nursing, hygiene, mothercraft, accident prevention, fire protection, messenger work and artificial respiration so that they may be trained and ready to help those in need.

6. Service to others is the keynote of the Junior Red Cross movement. In Australia, in the early days of the Junior Red Cross movement the young people raised enough money to furnish and equip houses for the children of ex-service men who were sick or in poor health. In Canada because of the shortage of dentists in Newfoundland, the Juniors raised funds to provide the people with a "floating" dental clinic. In summer, the boat carrying the dentist and his assistant sails the hundred and ninety miles of rugged coastline and in winter a snowmobile is used to visit the patients.

7. British Juniors help at holiday camps for physically handicapped children, where the young guests are given a real holiday, and, through taking part with Junior members in all the normal activities of camp life, are able to forget their disabilities so that they often return home able to do more for themselves. British Juniors also knit blankets for refugee children and for people in hospital, both in the United Kingdom and overseas. Junior Red Cross members visit and help the sick and elderly often doing the shopping for them.

They prepare "disaster relief kits" which are filled with specially selected contents and stored throughout the year ready to be sent at short notice to children who have lost everything in a disaster such as fire, hurricane or earthquake.

8. The Red Cross was originally formed to care for sick and wounded soldiers in time of war, but the fight against epidemics and disease is carried on all the time by National Red Cross Societies. The British Red Cross in its Overseas Branches is particularly concerned with the improvement of health and the prevention of disease. In countries such as Ceylon, Ghana, Malaya and Nigeria, which now have independent Societies of their own, though they were once part of the British Red Cross, Junior Members are actively engaged in teaching their companions how to grow strong and keep healthy. The newly formed Congolese Red Cross is one of those Societies which has brought hope to thousands through the medical treatment of leprosy. During the famine in 1961 Congo Juniors helped to distribute the milk bought

for starving children with money sent by many Red Cross Societies.

9. Blood transfusion is used a great deal by surgeons in operations and is responsible for saving many lives. The Red Cross is proud to help with this work. Some of the National Societies have blood banks, where supplies of the correct types of blood are available for hospitals to use whenever they are required. The Belgian Red Cross has a bone bank which has helped hundreds of people undergoing spinal operations. Another unusual activity has been established by the Siamese Red Cross which operates a snake farm to collect the serum used to cure those bitten by poisonous snakes.

10. First aid is closely associated with the Red Cross all over the world. When sporting events are held detachments of volunteers are present to render help to the victims of accidents. In factories, medical rooms are

established to deal with casualties among the workers; on the highways first aid posts have been set up. In South Africa and Russia a knowledge of first aid is necessary before workers are allowed to go down the mine-shafts. On many beaches in Britain and elsewhere, first aid posts are set up by the Red Cross to help holiday-makers in case of sudden illness or accident or injuries, such as cut feet.

11. The work done by the Red Cross brings comfort and happiness to many people especially the old, the sick and the disabled. Juniors visit and take gifts to them so bringing sunshine into their lives. Many members of the British Junior Red Cross have learnt the deaf-blind manual language, so that they may bring pleasure to those who cannot see or hear by talking to them through the touch language and by reading to them or writing letters for them.

12. The Red Cross spans the world. Today over eighty-five nations have Red Cross Societies, and by May 1961 the total membership had exceeded 140,000,000 people; men, women, boys and girls of every race and creed, all banded together to help suffering people.

13. The motto of the British Red Cross is "Inter Arma Caritas"—Charity in War; shortened version of "Inter Arma Fulget Ubique Caritas" which can be translated as "Everywhere in the midst of war shines forth love." The Red Cross is a symbol of world wide mercy in the struggle against human distress.

QUESTIONS ON THE STORY

1. Who founded the Red Cross?
2. Where was this person born?
3. Was he a poor man?
4. What profession did he follow on leaving school?
5. What battle did he watch?
6. Between which two countries was it fought?
7. In what way did Dunant seek to relieve suffering at Castiglione?
8. How were bandages made?
9. What name did the soldiers give Dunant?
10. What service did the boys and girls do to give help?
11. What was the title of Dunant's book?
12. What was the result of the publication of this book?
13. Describe at least one proposal put forward at the first meeting in Geneva.
14. How was the design for the Red Cross flag obtained?
15. Have all countries adopted this flag?
16. In what year were the Conventions brought up to date?
17. What was added to them in that year?
18. Name *four* instances when the Red Cross would act quickly to render aid to the injured and distressed?
19. What particular services are performed by the Red Cross in time of war?
20. What great scheme was operated in the last war for the benefit of civilians who were separated from their families?

QUESTIONS ON THE INTERESTING FACTS

1. Who was responsible for the founding of the Junior Red Cross?
2. What is the Motto of the Junior Red Cross, and what are its three aims?
3. Describe how the "Dental Clinic" sponsored by the Junior Red Cross in Newfoundland is able to reach outlying districts (*a*) in summer; (*b*) in winter?
4. How can Junior members help children who have lost everything in a flood, earthquake or hurricane?
5. Describe a Junior Red Cross activity which helps children who are physically handicapped.
6. How does the Junior Red Cross help sick and elderly people?
7. How can Junior members communicate with people who are both deaf and blind?
8. Which National Red Cross Society operates a snake farm to collect serum to cure people bitten by poisonous snakes?
9. What is a "Blood Bank".
10. Roughly how many Nations have Red Cross Societies today?

Further information and full particulars about membership of the Society, including how to join, may be obtained from your local Red Cross Branch, or from:

THE JUNIOR RED CROSS DEPARTMENT,
BRITISH RED CROSS SOCIETY,
14 GROSVENOR CRESCENT,
LONDON, S.W.1.

A Japanese Legend

There is a strange belief among the Japanese people that mirrors have souls. The reason for this belief is that they say that the mirror takes to itself, something of the owner's spirit, by constantly reflecting the person's image. They therefore treat mirrors with care and reverence, believing that from being used by so many generations, the mirror will reflect the various qualities of character of the people who used it. Mirrors have an honourable place in a Japanese household, and are never thrown away, but passed down from one generation to another.

Here is a short story which illustrates the high esteem in which some Japanese families held these fashionable articles of toilet.

THERE WAS A certain house in the town of Kyoto, which people avoided. The reason for their fear was that two of the former owners of the house had drowned themselves in the well that stood in the courtyard. Both of these tenants had apparently been very happy and there seemed no cause for them to commit suicide, yet both had become victims of some wicked spell.

The house had been lying empty for some time, as no one was willing to occupy a place with such a bad reputation, and so it was let very cheaply to Matsumura, a poor priest. He had come to the city to try to get a grant from the Regent for the restoration of the temple in his own country village.

Shortly after Matsumura took over the tenancy of the house, a great drought occurred in that area. Water became very scarce and many wells and reservoirs dried up. Matsumura's well was one of the few that did not go dry and he allowed many people to come and draw water from it.

One day there was an outcry in the courtyard. A young man had been found drowned in the well. Only then did Matsumura recall all the queer stories about this strange house. Once more, the people of the neighbourhood shunned the house and went to draw their water elsewhere, leaving Matsumura alone.

As he sat on the brink of the well, Matsumura kept turning these strange happenings over and over in his mind and there seemed to be no solution for these tragic occurrences. All at once, he started, for something white appeared in the dark water below. It reached the surface and was revealed as the face of a very beautiful woman. She smiled wistfully up at the priest. Matsumura felt his knees melt with fright. He had hardly strength to run from the well. When he had sufficiently recovered from the spell which she seemed to have cast over him, he called some men to help him to cover the well. They weighed the lid down with great stones and logs, so that no one else might fall a victim to the enchantress beneath.

That night, there came a knock at Matsumura's door. He opened it and saw the maid of the well standing in the moonlight. In spite of his terror, the priest cried, "Witch, what do you want? Why have you drawn people to their death? I shall call on the good spirit to drive you away."

The maiden stopped him and holding up her hands,

said, "Kind sir, I am no witch. I desired not the death of those good men. I only wanted their help. The water is low. Search for my body and then at last I shall be at rest".

So saying, she walked across the courtyard and despite the heavy cover, she melted into the well like a wisp of smoke.

Matsumura spent a troubled night thinking on the plight of the phantom maid and wondering what the outcome of it all would be. Early next morning he told his story to the neighbours, who, though they remained doubtful, were willing to help him explore the mysteries of the well. When they had searched the well thoroughly, all that they found was a mirror covered with mud and slime.

Matsumura did not scoff at the discovery like the

others. He carefully cleaned it and found that it was made of silver. On the back, beneath an engraving of the sacred mountain, there were inscriptions which he could not read save for a few scattered dates and names. He wrapped the mirror in a cloth and put it away, waiting for the maiden, who, he felt sure, would return.

Sure enough, one evening he raised his eyes from his holy book to see her standing before him again. "Kind priest," she said, "I thank you for your rescue and your care of me. I am the soul of the mirror. I belonged in ancient times to Lady Kamo of the Imperial Court and had been an heirloom in her family for many years. One day however, a jealous lady, in a fit of spite, threw me into that well. After reflecting so much beauty and gladness, sunshine and colour, I lay in the darkness far from human touch. I was wretched. I longed to escape. Oh priest, give me to Lord Yoshimasa, the descendant of my first mistress and I shall be happy again." With these words, she vanished.

Lord Yoshimasa was the Regent of the province and he was the one with whom Matsumura had long sought an audience. The priest set out with the mirror next day and went up to the Regent's palace, saying that he wished to restore an heirloom that belonged to the Regent. He was brought into his presence and Lord Yoshimasa was so pleased with the story that he accepted the mirror and readily agreed to grant the money to restore the temple.

Matsumura, his mission completed, returned to his village with the joyful news. The mirror spent the rest of its days happily, for it remained in the possession of Yoshimasa's little daughter, who treated it with the loving care it deserved.

INTERESTING FACTS ON
JAPAN AND THE JAPANESE

1. Many names are given to the country we know as Japan. Marco Polo first introduced Japan to the people of Europe as a wonderland of treasure, which he called "*Zipangu*". To the Chinese, gazing eastwards, it was "the land of the Rising Sun," though the Japanese themselves call their country, *Nippon*. It is also "the land of the cherry blossom" for that flower is the national flower of Japan. Sometimes Japan is referred to as the British Isles of the Pacific. This is because both countries consist of islands near a large continent and both are nations of sailors and traders. The *rising sun* emblem is shown on the Japanese ensign.

2. Almost ninety million people are crowded into the four islands of *Honshu, Hokkaido, Shikoku* and *Kyushu*, which make up Japan. Not only are the islands small but they are mountainous and have little arable land. To compensate for the lack of low ground, the Japanese

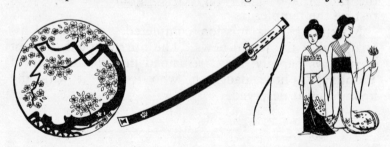

174

have created wide terraces up the hillsides and these are intensely cultivated. This island empire has an extensive coastline and *fishing* is an important industry. *Rice* is grown on the plains, while *tea* and mulberry bushes are mainly cultivated on the terraces.

3. Though land is so scarce, the Japanese are keen gardeners and many of them have become expert in giving an illusion of space to tiny bits of land. For example the skilled gardener will know, where to place a miniature waterfall. how to sling an artificial bridge and where to hang a stone lantern, so as to achieve the effect of an enlarged garden. *Nikko*, a city of shrines and gardens, near the capital city of Tokyo, attracts many visitors. Statues of Buddha, temples and museums are set amongst the luxuriant trees and flowering shrubs in a large national park. From one of the elaborately carved memorials there, comes the *"see-no-evil, hear-no-evil, speak-no-evil"* motto, copies of which have been circulated throughout the world.

4. The Japanese are very fond of flowers and many of our own favourite flowers came originally from Japan. Holidays are set apart so that people can go out to admire the fruit trees in flower, the *cherry, plum* and *peach* blossoms. Men and women, old and young all dress up in their best clothes to visit these colourful fields of *irises* and *lilies*, gardens of *roses, azaleas, purple wistaria* and *camellia*. Trees also receive great attention in

Japan, the graceful *bamboo* canes forming a background of fairy wands to the stately *pine* and *lacquer* trees.

5. *Earthquakes* and the eruptions of active *volcanoes* are a constant danger in Japan. To guard against this, houses are made of light materials, so that if they fall or are destroyed, it will be less dangerous and no great loss will be incurred. This precaution however makes houses more liable to catch fire. In 1923, the capital city of *Tokyo* and its port of *Yokohama*, were almost completely destroyed by an earthquake, and besides the enormous loss of life, over a million people were rendered homeless. The most famous volcano in Japan is the sacred *Fujiyama*, "fire mountain", and most Japanese make at least one pilgrimage up this picturesque mountain. It appears in many Japanese drawings and decorations.

6. The Japanese are a most artistic race and are excellent copyists. Besides the delicate *paintings* and exquisite *lacquer-ware*, much of their work can be seen on the screens, fans and embroideries that are exported all over the world. They are very skilled in hand-loom weaving, the making of *silk* and in *pottery* painting. Japanese *porcelain* has a world renown and surpasses the modern products of China, from where the art was first learned. They are especially noted for making delicate products, such as *toys*. Their *swords* are also justly famous. Japan has not been slow to copy Western ideas and being an island country, *shipbuilding* is a great industry; indeed her mercantile fleet is one of the largest in the world.

7. The women of Japan are fonder of the traditional dress than the men, who have copied the Western style of clothes. The *Kimono*, a kind of silk or satin dressing gown, with wide sleeves, and a broad sash or *"obi"*, is still the distinctive garment of the country. The sleeves and sash serve as pockets. Shoes are worn over thick socks and are removed, when entering a house, so as not to soil the mats which are used for sitting on. A Japanese house contains little furniture. There are no chairs and the beds are thick quilts laid on the floor with wooden pillows which are removed during daytime. The walls are made of light wood or tough paper with sliding doors serving as partitions. At meals each person sits on a cushion and is served separately on a little lacquer tray.

8. Japanese children are trained from infancy to be self-controlled and polite as well as to be gentle and happy in their ways. There are few miserable or selfish children in Japan, for they have so many interesting things to do. Their favourite toys are *dolls*, *tops*, and *kites*. There are special feast days for children when toys of all kinds are brought out. The *Feast of the Dolls* is for girls, and the dolls, many of which are kept from generation to generation, are produced and all sorts of games are played. The boys hold the *Feast of the Flags*, when they buy flags, helmets, wooden-horses, bows and arrows, and dress up like the heroes of long ago. The big event of this festival is a sham fight between two picked sides. One of the most important festival processions takes place at the *New Year*, for age in Japan is reckoned from the New Year, not the actual birthday.

9. Among the many qualities that distinguish the Japanese from other races are the ability to endure hardship or pain, the "poker-face" that shows no sign of emotion, and, above all their extreme politeness. Though inwardly a warm-hearted happy people, they keep themselves very stiff and serious. When two Japanese meet, they click their heels, press their hands to their sides and bow at least six times. The person who is of lesser importance bows a little lower and stays down a little longer. Their religion, called *Shinto*, meaning "the way of the gods" teaches them loyalty to their Emperor, who is supposed to be a divine figure descended from the Sun goddess. Recent changes have meant that the Emperor is no longer regarded as a god, but the idea of loyalty to their superior still lives on.

10. Their religion also teaches courage, even courage to take one's own life. As they believe when they die that they join their honourable ancestors and become guardian spirits of their homeland, they do not find it so hard to commit suicide or "hara-kiri" as it is called. *Geisha* girls are trained from their early years in music, dancing, singing and the art of witty and amusing conversation. They are employed as hostesses by rich merchants and business firms. The Japanese science of self-defence without weapons is known as "ju-jitsu" or "judo". It is a form of wrestling in which a skilled wrestler can, by tripping or throwing, overcome a stronger and heavier opponent. Judo is part of a Western soldier's training in unarmed combat.

QUESTIONS ON THE STORY

1. What strange belief do Japanese have about mirrors?
2. Why do they hold this belief?
3. What happens to mirrors in Japan?
4. Why was the house in Kyoto avoided?
5. Why was Matsumura able to rent the house cheaply?
6. What was Matsumura's purpose in coming to Kyoto?
7. What occurrence brought the people back to Matsumura's house?
8. What happened after they came back?
9. What appeared to Matsumura at the well?
10. Why did he cover up the well?
11. What happened that night?
12. What did the phantom maid ask Matsumura to do?
13. What did they find in the well?
14. What was inscribed on the back of the mirror?
15. What was Matsumura doing when the maiden appeared again?
16. Tell the maid's story as to how she came to be in the well.
17. Who was the descendant of her first mistress and what connection had he with with Matsumura?
18. What happened when Matsumura went to the Regent's palace?
19. Why would the villagers be pleased to see Matsumura on his return?
20. What happened to the mirror?

QUESTIONS ON THE INTERESTING FACTS

1. (a) Give three names for Japan.
   (b) In what ways does Japan resemble Britain?
2. (a) Name the islands that form Japan.
   (b) How do the Japanese make up for the lack of low land for cultivation?
   (c) Name three products of Japan.
3. (a) In what ways can a Japanese gardener make a small garden appear large?
   (b) Name a well-known ornament that comes from the carvings at Nikko.
4. (a) Name two kinds of flowers and trees in Japan.
   (b) How do you know that the Japanese are fond of flowers?
5. (a) Name two great natural dangers in Japan.
   (b) Why do the Japanese build their houses of light materials?
   (c) What took place in the great Japanese earthquake of 1923?
   (d) Name the sacred mountain of Japan.
6. (a) Name three occupations in which the Japanese are highly skilled.
   (b) In what industrial way has Japan not been slow to copy Western ideas?
7. (a) What is a "kimono"? What is an "obi"?
   (b) Why are shoes removed before entering a Japanese house?
   (c) Where do Japanese people sleep?
   (d) How are meals served in a Japanese home?
8. (a) Why are there so few miserable children in Japan?
   (b) Name two interesting festivals for Japanese children.
   (c) From what time of year do the Japanese calculate their ages?

9. (a) Name three qualities that distinguish the Japanese from other races.
    (b) What is the Japanese religion called?
    (c) From whom is the Emperor descended?
10. (a) What is "hara-kiri"?
    (b) Who employs "geisha" girls?
    (c) Who, in modern times, receive training in "judo"?

DEVELOPMENT EXERCISES

1. Point out on the map:—
    Asia, Japan, China, Tokyo, Fujiyama.
2. Either   Invent a story of a "ghost" lady, who was shut up in the tower of a castle.
    Or   Tell the sad tale of a broken mirror.
3. The Japanese hold a festival on New Year's Day. With what date are the following connected:—
    (a) Guy Fawkes' Day; (b) Hallowe'en; (c) Hogmanay; (d) Remembrance Day; (e) St. Patrick's Day?
4. The religion of the Japanese is called Shinto. What is the religion of each of the following races:—
    (a) Arabs; (b) English; (c) Hebrews; (d) Hindus; (e) Russians?
5. Write a short paragraph showing the differences between a home in Britain and one in Japan.
6. Fujiyama is the sacred mountain of Japan. Where are the following sacred places:—
    (a) Benares; (b) Lhasa; (c) Lourdes; (d) Jerusalem; (e) Mecca?
7. Judo is a form of unarmed combat. What name is given to the sport in which the following are used:—
    (a) clubs; (b) foils; (c) gloves; (d) racquets; (e) wickets?
8. The Japanese are very fond of flowers. Make a list of (a) garden flowers, and (b) wild flowers.

ROUGH JUSTICE

By his writings Charles Dickens brought to light many injustices that existed at the beginning of the nineteenth century. In his book "Oliver Twist", he exposed the dreadful conditions among the very poor in London. This episode tells of what happens when the orphan Oliver is caught after running away from the scene where his new-found friends, who were pick-pockets, had stolen a handkerchief from a gentleman.—(ADAPTED.)

THE offence had been committed within the district, and indeed in the immediate neighbourhood of, a very notorious metropolitan police-office. The crowd had only the satisfaction of accompanying Oliver through two or three streets, and down a place called Mutton Hill, when he was led beneath a low archway, and up a dirty court, into this dispensary of summary justice, by the backway. It was a small paved yard into which they turned; and here they encountered a stout man with a bunch of whiskers on his face and a bunch of keys in his hand.

"What's the matter now?" said the man carelessly.

"A young fogle hunter," replied the man who had Oliver in charge.

"Are you the party that's been robbed, sir?" inquired the man with the keys.

"Yes, I am," replied the old gentleman; "but I am not sure that this boy actually took the handkerchief. I-I would rather not press the case."

"Must go before the magistrate now, sir," replied the man. "His Worship will be disengaged in half a minute. Now, young gallows!"

This was an invitation for Oliver to enter through a door. which he unlocked as he spoke, and which led into a stone cell. Here he was searched; and nothing being found upon him, locked up.

This cell was in shape and size something like an area cellar, only not so light. It was most intolerably dirty. The old gentleman looked almost as rueful as Oliver when the key grated in the lock. He turned with a sigh to the book, which had been the innocent cause of all this disturbance.

"There is something in that boy's face," said the old gentleman to himself, as he walked slowly away, tapping his chin with the cover of the book in a thoughtful manner, "something that touches and interests me. *Can* he be innocent?"

After musing for some minutes, the old gentleman walked, with the same meditative face, into a back ante-room opening from the yard. He heaved a sigh and being, happily for himself, an absent-minded old gentleman, buried his thoughts in the pages of the musty book.

He was roused by a touch on the shoulder, and a request from the man with the keys to follow him into the office. He closed his book hastily; and was at once ushered into the imposing presence of the renowned Mr. Fang.

The office was a front parlour, with a panelled wall. Mr. Fang sat behind a bar, at the upper end; and on one side of the door was a sort of wooden pen in which poor little Oliver was already deposited, trembling very much at the awfulness of the scene.

Mr. Fang was a lean, long-backed, stiff-necked, middle-sized man, with no great quantity of hair, and what he had, growing on the back and sides of his head. His face was stern, and much flushed.

The old gentleman bowed respectfully; and, advancing to the magistrate's desk, said, suiting the action to the word, "That is my name and address, sir." He then withdrew a pace or two; and, with another polite and gentlemanly inclination of the head, waited to be questioned.

Now it so happened that Mr. Fang was at that moment out of temper; and he looked up with an angry scowl.

"Who are you?" said Mr. Fang.

The old gentleman pointed, with some surprise, to his card.

"Officer!" said Mr. Fang, tossing the card contemptuously away, "Who is this fellow?"

"My name, sir," said the old gentleman, speaking *like* a gentleman, "my name, sir, is Brownlow. Permit me to inquire the name of the magistrate who offers a gratuitous and unprovoked insult to a respectable person, under the protection of the bench." Saying this, Mr. Brownlow looked around the office as if in search of some person who would afford him the required information.

"Officer!" said Mr. Fang, throwing the paper on one side, "What's this fellow charged with?"

"He's not charged at all, your Worship," replied the officer. "He appears against the boy, your Worship."

His Worship knew this perfectly well; but it was a good annoyance, and a safe one.

"Appears against the boy, does he?" said Mr. Fang, surveying Mr. Brownlow contemptuously from head to foot. "Swear him!"

"Before I am sworn, I must beg to say one word," said Mr. Brownlow: "and that is, that I really never, without actual experience, could have believed——"

"Hold your tongue, sir!" said Mr. Fang peremptorily.

"I will not, sir!" replied the old gentleman.

"Hold your tongue this instant, or I'll have you turned out of the office!" said Mr. Fang. "You're an insolent, impertinent fellow. How dare you bully a magistrate!"

"What!" exclaimed the old gentleman, reddening.

"Swear this person!" said Fang to the clerk. "I'll not hear another word. Swear him."

Mr. Brownlow's indignation was greatly roused; but reflecting perhaps, that he might only injure the boy by giving vent to it, he suppressed his feelings and submitted to be sworn at once

"Now," said Mr. Fang, "what's the charge against this boy? What have you got to say, sir?"

"I was standing at a bookstall——" Mr. Brownlow began.

"Hold your tongue, sir," said Mr. Fang. "Policeman! Where's the policeman? Here, swear this policeman. Now, policeman, what is this?"

The policeman, with becoming humility, related how

he had taken the charge; how he had searched Oliver, and found nothing on his person; and how that was all he knew about it.

"Are there any witnesses?" inquired Mr. Fang.

"None, your Worship," replied the policeman.

Mr. Fang sat silent for some minutes, and then, turning to the prosecutor, said in a towering passion:

"Do you mean to state what your complaint against this boy is, man, or do you not? You have been sworn. Now, if you stand there, refusing to give evidence, I'll punish you for disrespect to the bench."

With many interruptions, and repeated insults, Mr. Brownlow contrived to state his case; observing that, in the surprise of the moment, he had run after the boy because he had seen him running away; and expressing his hope, that if the magistrate should believe him, although not actually the thief, to be connected with thieves, he would deal as leniently with him as justice would allow.

"He has been hurt already," said the old gentleman in conclusion. "And I fear," he added with great energy, looking towards the bar, "I really fear that he is ill."

"Oh! yes, I dare say!" said Mr. Fang with a sneer. "Come, none of your tricks here, you young vagabond; they won't do. What's your name?"

Oliver tried to reply, but his tongue failed him. He was deadly pale; and the whole place seemed turning round and round.

"What's your name, you hardened scoundrel?" demanded Mr. Fang. "Officer, what's his name?"

This was addressed to a bluff old fellow, in a striped waistcoat, who was standing by the bar. He bent over Oliver, and repeated the inquiry; but finding him really incapable of understanding the question, and knowing that his not replying would only infuriate the magistrate the more, and add to the severity of his sentence; he hazarded a guess.

"He says his name's Tom White, your Worship," said this kind-hearted thief-taker.

"Oh, he won't speak out, won't he?" said Fang. "Very well, very well. Where does he live?"

"Where he can, your Worship," replied the officer, again pretending to receive Oliver's answer.

"Has he any parents?" inquired Mr. Fang.

"He says they died in his infancy, your Worship," hazarding the usual reply.

At this point of the inquiry, Oliver raised his head; and, looking round with imploring eyes, murmured a feeble prayer for a draught of water.

"Stuff and nonsense!" said Mr. Fang: "don't try to make a fool of me."

"I think he really is ill, your Worship," remonstrated the officer.

"I know better," said Mr. Fang.

"Take care of him, officer," said the old gentleman, raising his hands instinctively; "he'll fall down."

"Stand away, officer," cried Fang; "let him, if he likes."

Oliver availed himself of the kind permission, and fell to the floor in a fainting fit. The men in the office looked at each other, but no one dared to stir.

"I knew he was shamming," said Fang, as if this were incontestable proof of the fact. "Let him lie there; he'll soon be tired of that."

"How do you propose to deal with the case, sir?" inquired the clerk in a low voice.

"Summarily," replied Mr. Fang. "He stands committed for three months—hard labour, of course. Clear the office."

The door was opened for this purpose, and a couple of men were preparing to carry the insensible boy to his cell, when an elderly man of decent but poor appearance, clad in an old suit of black, rushed hastily into the office, and advanced towards the bench.

"Stop, stop! Don't take him away! For Heaven's sake, stop a moment!" cried the newcomer, breathless with haste.

"What is this? Who is this? Turn this man out. Clear the office!" cried Mr. Fang.

"I *will* speak," cried the man; "I will not be turned out. I saw it all. I keep the book-stall. I demand to be sworn. I will not be put down. Mr. Fang, you must hear me. You must not refuse, sir."

The man was right. His manner was determined; and the matter was growing rather too serious to be hushed up.

"Swear the man," growled Mr. Fang, with a very ill grace. "Now, man, what have you got to say?"

"This," said the man: "I saw three boys—two others and the prisoner here—loitering on the opposite side of the way, when this gentleman was reading. The robbery was committed by another boy. I saw it done; and I saw that this boy was perfectly amazed and stupefied by it." Having by this time recovered a little breath, the worthy book-stall keeper proceeded to relate, in a more coherent manner, the exact circumstances of the robbery.

"Why didn't you come here before?" said Mr. Fang, after a pause.

"I hadn't a soul to mind the shop," replied the man. "Everybody who could have helped me had joined in the pursuit. I could get nobody till five minutes ago; and I've run here all the way."

"The prosecutor was reading, was he?" inquired Fang after another pause.

"Yes," replied the man. "The very book he has in his hand."

"Oh, that book, eh?" said Fang. "Is it paid for?"

"No, it is not," replied the man, with a smile.

"Dear me, I forgot all about it!" exclaimed the absent old gentleman innocently.

"A nice person to prefer a charge against a poor boy!" said Fang with a comical effort to look humane. "I consider, sir, that you have obtained possession of that book, under very suspicious and disreputable circumstances; and you may think yourself very fortunate that the owner of the property declines to prosecute. Let this be a lesson to you, my man, or the law will overtake you yet. The boy is discharged. Clear the office."

The indignant Mr. Brownlow was conveyed out, with the book in his hand, in a perfect frenzy of rage

and defiance. He reached the yard; and his passion
vanished in a moment. Little Oliver Twist lay on his
back on the pavement, with his shirt unbuttoned, and
his temples bathed with water; his face a deadly white;
and a cold tremble convulsing his whole frame.

"Poor boy, poor boy!" said Mr. Brownlow, bending
over him. "Call a coach, somebody, pray. Directly!"

A coach was obtained, and Oliver having been carefully laid on one seat, the old gentleman got in and sat
on the other.

"May I accompany you?" said the book-stall keeper,
looking in.

"Bless me, yes, my dear sir," said Mr. Brownlow
quickly. "I forgot you. Dear, dear! I have this unhappy book still! Jump in. Poor fellow! There's no
time to lose."

The book-stall keeper got into the coach; and away
they drove.

INTERESTING FACTS ON THE LAW

1. "No freeman shall be imprisoned unless by the judgment of his peers or by the law of the land." This was one of the main points in the *Magna Carta* (Great Charter) which King John signed in 1215, and this document is regarded as the foundation of the personal freedom of the individual in Britain. The *goddess of Justice* is always pictured as being blindfolded to show her impartiality. She also has the sword of justice in one hand and a pair of scales in the other. The scales represent the fairness of balance by which judgment is made.

2. In serious cases, *trial by jury* is the recognised method by which an accused person is tried. A jury consists of twelve men and women in civil actions, and fifteen in criminal cases. They listen to the evidence of both sides before coming to a decision. After the cases have been stated, the judge advises the jury on the law and reminds the jury that by British law, a person is considered innocent until he is proved guilty. One of the jury, whom they have elected as *foreman*, declares the jury's decision to the judge.

3. An accused person may have the services of a lawyer, termed attorney or *counsel for the defence*. If the crime is a breach of the law of the country, the crime is said to be against the crown and *prosecuting counsel* puts the case against the accused. The witnesses give their evidence *under oath*. In England with left hand on the Bible and right hand upraised, they swear "by Almighty God, to tell the truth, the whole truth and nothing but the truth." In Scotland the Bible is not used when the oath is administered.

4. The jury pronounces the verdict and the judge imposes the punishment to fit the crime. The system of administering justice varies in each country. In England, *Quarter Sessions* are courts in which the tried cases are not so serious as those that go before the *Assize Courts*. In cities the Session judge is known as a *Recorder*, who is generally a barrister—in Scotland, an advocate—or a lawyer of wide experience, who has "taken silk". In England also, the *coroner* is an official or doctor trained in the law, whose duty it is to make inquiry into the death of any person who may have died from other than natural causes. Minor cases are also tried by a *Sheriff*, *Justice of the Peace* or *Magistrate*, and the more serious cases by *Lords of the Court of Justice*. *Courts* are arranged to coincide with the circuits of these High Court judges, who visit each part of the country, when required.

5. An accused person may *appeal* against a sentence. The appeal can be made to a higher court of justice or in certain cases to the House of Lords, and the sentence can be altered or overturned. The president of the highest court of appeal in the Empire, and the greatest legal authority in Britain, is the *Lord Chancellor*. He acts as *Speaker* in the House of Lords and is a member of the Cabinet. His official seat in the House of Lords is the *Woolsack*, which is a square bag of wool covered in red cloth. It dates back to the time of Queen Elizabeth and is a reminder of the national importance of the wool trade.

6. When the law breaks down *Anarchy* occurs, as at the French Revolution, when the existing laws were swept away and replaced by a very harsh and crude system. Judges exercise the law impartially, but the notorious Chief Justice Jeffreys, in what were called the

"Bloody Assizes", of 1685, used his power to condemn people to death or sentence them to transportation for trivial offences.

7. The first colonisation of *Australia* was mainly by convicts who had been shipped from Britain. They worked in prison labour settlements, particularly at *Botany Bay* near Sydney. When they were released, they settled down in the country as law-abiding citizens. The most infamous of all penal settlements was *Devil's Island*, off the coast of French Guiana in South America.

8. Before a person is tried, he may be released on *bail*, that is on payment of a sum of money as a guarantee that he will stand trial. If he fails to attend, the money is forfeited and a warrant may be issued for his arrest. Young people convicted of misdemeanours may be put under the supervision of a Probation officer or they may be sent to an *approved* school, but if further offences are committed, they can be sent to a *Borstal* institution. These places try to show the offenders the errors of their ways and to teach them how to become good citizens.

9. When a person is *acquitted*, this means he is free and that he cannot be tried again for the same offence. In England, a person may be *Guilty* or *Not Guilty*, but in Scotland, a third, verdict of *Not Proven* is sometimes used, and this means that there was not sufficient evidence, to make a decision one way or the other.

10. Punishments vary according to the gravity of the crimes. When a prisoner receives a short sentence he is held in one of the smaller prisons, but if he is convicted of a major crime, he is usually sent to one of the out-of-the-way prisons, like Dartmoor or Peterhead, for a long term. A person who is given a *life* sentence, usually serves about fifteen years with time taken off for good conduct while in prison.

QUESTIONS ON THE STORY

1. Who wrote the story?
2. Where did the episode take place?
3. Of what was Oliver accused?
4. What happened to him when he reached the court?
5. Give the magistrate's name and describe his appearance.
6. In what way did he make the old gentleman angry?
7. Why did the old gentleman not wish to prosecute Oliver?
8. Why did the court officer give Oliver another name?
9. What evidence is there to show that Mr. Fang was a cruel man?
10. What happened to show that Oliver was in a weak condition?
11. What sentence did Mr. Fang impose?
12. Who arrived to say that he had witnessed the incident?
13. What actually happened at the book-stall?
14. Why had the book-stall keeper been so late in coming forward?
15. Give an instance to show that the old gentleman was absent-minded.
16. What change did Mr. Fang make to his original sentence on Oliver?
17. In what way did Mr. Fang try to discredit Mr. Brownlow?
18. What had happened to Oliver after he fainted?
19. What did Mr. Brownlow do?
20. Who were in the coach?

QUESTIONS ON THE INTERESTING FACTS

1. (a) What is regarded as the foundation of British liberty?
   (b) Why is the goddess of Justice blindfolded?
   (c) What does she hold in each hand?
2. (a) How many jurors are there in a criminal assault case?
   (b) Of what does the judge remind the jury before they consider their verdict?
   (c) What name is given to the spokesman for the jury?
3. (a) Who defends an accused person?
   (b) Who states the case for the crown?
   (c) How does a person give evidence?
4. (a) Who imposes the punishment on a prisoner?
   (b) Name two minor court judges.
   (c) How do the High Court judges manage to cover the country?
5. (a) To whom can a convicted person appeal?
   (b) Who is the highest legal authority in Britain?
   (c) Why is the Woolsack kept in the House of Lords?
6. (a) What happens when a country is in a state of anarchy?
   (b) Name a notorious judge of the seventeenth century.
7. (a) Who first colonised Australia?
   (b) Name a notorious penal settlement.
8. (a) What happens to a person if he fails to stand trial?
   (b) Name two places to which young offenders may be sent?
   (c) What do these institutions try to teach young offenders?
9. (a) What is meant when a person is "acquitted?"

    (*b*) What are the two verdicts in English law?

    (*c*) In what country is there a "not proven" verdict?

10. (*a*) Name a prison to which long-term prisoners may be sent?

    (*b*) How long is a life sentence in Britain?

DEVELOPMENT EXERCISES

1. What is the function of each of the following in a court of law, (*a*) a judge; (*b*) a jury; (*c*) a prosecutor; (*d*) a witness; (*e*) a defending counsel?

2. EITHER (*a*) You have been wrongly accused of breaking a window. Give a short account of what actually occurred.

    OR   (*b*) You see a burglar climbing through the window of a house. Tell briefly what you did and what happened.

3. The magistrate was referred to as His Worship. What form of address is used for each of the following: (*a*) a duchess; (*b*) an ambassador; (*c*) a Prime Minister; (*d*) a queen, (*e*) an archbishop?

4. Judges usually wear scarlet and ermine robes. What colours do you associate with each of the following people: (*a*) a bride; (*b*) a policeman; (*c*) a mourner; (*d*) a cardinal; (*e*) a soldier?

5. Explain the difference between a criminal case and a civil case.

6. The Lord Chancellor is the leading legal authority in Britain. Of what are each of the following in charge: (*a*) Chancellor of the Exchequer; (*b*) Post-master-General; (*c*) Foreign Secretary; (*d*) Minister of Agriculture; (*e*) First Lord of the Admiralty?

7. A life sentence in Britain is usually about fifteen years. How long are each of the following: (*a*) a century; (*b*) a decade; (*c*) a fortnight; (*d*) a leap year; (*e*) a lunar month?

8. Write a short note showing the meaning of (*a*) Guilty; (*b*) Not Guilty; (*c*) Not Proven.

9. Oliver Twist was known as "the boy who asked for more". Who were each of the following people: (*a*) the boy who never grew up; (*b*) the boy who could not tell a lie; (*c*) the soldier who held the bridge; (*d*) the sailor who turned a blind eye; (*e*) the saint who loved birds and flowers?

10. Charles Dickens was, by his writings, a great social reformer of the early nineteenth century. Find out who were connected with great reforms in (*a*) nursing; (*b*) prisons; (*c*) women's franchise; (*d*) factories; (*e*) slavery?

THE OLD GREY SQUIRREL

A great while ago there was a schoolboy
He lived in a cottage by the sea,
And the very first thing he could remember
Was the rigging of the schooners by the quay.

He could watch them, when he woke, from his window,
With the tall cranes hoisting out the freight,
And he used to think of shipping as a sea-cook,
And sailing to the Golden Gate.

For he used to buy the yellow penny dreadfuls.
And read them when he fished for conger-eels,
And listened to the lapping of the water,
The green and oily water round the keels.

There were trawlers with their shark-mouthed flat-fish,
And red nets hanging out to dry,
And the skate the skipper kept because he liked 'em,
And landsmen never knew the fish to fry.

There were brigantines with timber out of Norroway,
Oozing with the syrups of the pine.
There were rusty dusty schooners out of Sunderland,
And ships of the Blue Funnel line.

And to tumble down a hatch into the cabin
Was better than the best of broken rules;
For the smell of 'em was like a Christmas dinner,
And the feel of 'em was like a box of tools.

And, before he went to sleep in the evening,
The very last thing that he could see
Was the sailor-men a-dancing in the moonlight
By the capstan that stood upon the quay.

He is perched upon a high stool in London,
The Golden Gate is very far away.
They caught him, and they caged him, like a squirrel.
He is totting up accounts, and going grey.

He will never, never, never sail to 'Frisco.
But the very last thing that he will see
Will be sailor-men a-dancing in the sunrise
By the capstan that stands upon the quay . . .

To the tune of an old concertina,
By the capstan that stands upon the quay.

by ALFRED NOYES

KARIBA

The construction of the largest man-made lake in the world, half the size of Northern Ireland, was achieved by building a dam, four hundred and twenty feet in height, across the Zambesi River at Kariba Gorge. This huge reservoir lies partly in Zambia and partly in Zimbabwe.

The harnessing of the waters of the fifteen hundred mile long river will enable power to be brought to the Copper Belt and the rapidly expanding industries of a large area of Central Africa.

Apart from the wonderful engineering feat that was accomplished, over fifty thousand inhabitants and countless animals had to be removed to areas not threatened by the flood.

Transport was provided for the tribesmen, their

families and their possessions and they were taken to newly-constructed villages. Boats were used to remove the animals, trapped on the many islands, which would soon disappear beneath the rising waters.

It is part of this humane story of animal rescue that you are now going to read.

TAED EDELMAN decided to tackle Elephant Island on 6th June. His boat and the barge were loaded to the scuppers with as many men as possible (to act as beaters), and all the ropes, thunderflashes and whatever tackle was thought to be necessary for doing a job which most people seemed to believe was impossible : the rescue of the biggest of big game—elephants.

We started the engines shortly after dawn, put out on the pearly lake and steered into the rising sun along a crimson lane. It took only twenty minutes to get to Elephant Island, and when we did arrive the plan was for

Taed, Dick Link and Noel Verander to make a first reconnaissance before putting anyone else ashore to crash about in the undergrowth and startle the quarry.

Dick Link was a new helper. A grizzled Zimbabwean of fifty or so, he was an interesting character, with the sort of story one only finds in romantic novels. Five years ago he had been critically ill in hospital. He had an incurable cancer. One day his doctors came to his bedside and told him that he could expect to live only a few months more. " Go home," they said, " and settle up your affairs."

He did go home from hospital, but on the way he was startled to hear a disembodied voice say to him : " You're going to be all right." He took the voice at its word and never did settle his affairs. Now here he was stripped to the waist, his brown body smudged with livid scars where the sawbones had cut him up to catch his cancer. *That* had evaded them, and he had evaded *it*.

As usual, the barge was left behind and we could see its prow bumping and cutting into our wash, throwing up splinters of light as the waves broke on either side of the cut water.

Elephant Island was a long ridge of scrub and trees through which the sun shone like a lamp through a grating. For many days the ridge had been joined to the Northern Zimbabwean bank of the new lake as a peninsula. The swelling waves, however, had lapped over a saddle in the promontory and quickly turned the peninsula into an island. The lake over the narrow strait between island and mainland was at this time some ten feet deep.

Taed Edelman's hope was that any elephants marooned on the island could be driven by beaters into taking to the water at the straits and so would either wade or swim across. For elephants can swim, and usually do so with most of their body and head submerged, while the end of the trunk pokes vertically above the surface and acts as a schnorkel tube for breathing.

We were careful to approach the island from the
leeward side for an obvious reason. If the elephants were
still there, we didn't want to alarm them by allowing the
wind to carry our scent in their direction. As usual, there
were tree-tops sticking out of the lake, drowning before

their neighbours a little higher up the slopes. Taed shut off the engines and our boat glided noiselessly among the trees, where we moored to remain hidden. Then he, Dick and Noel waded ashore while the rest of us waited.

After half an hour, the reconnaissance party returned with the news that there appeared to be three full-grown cow elephants and two babies still on the island.

We all disembarked from the launches and a line of thirty Africans and five Europeans, spaced out at intervals, began to move through the crackling bush and trees. Everybody made as much noise as possible and every now and then someone would let off a thunderflash in the hope of driving the elephants in front of us. There was extra danger in the situation because the presence of the babies meant that one of the strongest of all animal instincts, the mother's instinct for protecting her young, would be called into play.

The babel of noise moved slowly forward, a sort of creeping barrage of dust and din which seemed to be driving the three elephants and their calves up to the point of the island reaching out to Northern Zimbabwe and freedom—if they had only known it.

The mother was in a terrible predicament; for she was no doubt terrified of the racket, but she was probably even more terrified of having to force her infants into the waters of the lake. Suddenly one of the beaters rushed forward in a burst of wild enthusiasm. Her mind made up, she flung forward her trunk like an uncurled watch spring and charged at the frantic brown body which had tantalised her to breaking-point. Her thick stumps of legs criss-crossed at what seemed to me incredible speed and I thought the African was done for. How he escaped that moving mountain I just wasn't able to see, but he did so ; and as his neighbours fell over each other to right and to left, thinking now only of escape, a gap of some twenty yards appeared in the beaters' line. The first elephant was

already crashing through it, followed closely by her
bouncing daughters and, in a flash, the others had crossed
the gap.

Taed called a halt for a meal. As we ate, he expounded
another plan. The splitting-up of the herd seemed to be
fairly easy to achieve, but the next and most difficult
phase of the operation was to separate one of the baby
elephants from its mother ; to keep the mother out of
the way and capture the daughter—literally capture her
by fastening ropes round her legs so that she could be led
into the water and forced to cross the strait. Once she
was on the mainland she would be freed. Her bellowings
would attract her mother ; she would swim the narrow
channel of water and the other two cows and baby would
probably follow. It all seemed so simple—and so
dangerous. It was decided to try it.

As it turned out, this plan worked, more or less. It was,
in fact, the lake itself which really helped. The mother
kept her offspring behind her at some distance, always
making certain that her huge bulk was between us and the
two young cows. This was really her undoing, for the
rising lake quite suddenly formed an islet between the
mainland and the larger island and, by a stroke of good
fortune for us, the older baby was cut off and left stranded
on this islet. Mother and daughter were separated and the
young elephant was overwhelmed by a bunch of twelve
natives who splashed over to the little island, urged on by
Tom and Noel. An almost continuous roar of thunderflashes kept the others running.

The young elephant spun this way and that, charged
forwards, jumped backwards, not daring to enter the
water, and men hung on to the trunk, tail, ears and legs.
There were so many people on her that she disappeared
like a ball in a rugby scrum. When they let her get up,
she was held at six points—ropes round each leg, a rope
round her neck and one boy held her tail. Now she

looked like some grotesque spider at the centre of her web or like Gulliver, when the Lilliputians bound him with threads.

The rope-holders forced her to the water's edge and, wrench and jerk as she might, she had to go in. For fifty yards she was able to walk, then she had to swim for it ; so did the elephant tamers. In five minutes Jumbo had reached the mainland bank, and, a little exhausted and stupefied, she stood quietly letting the water trickle off her grey hide, while the captors, breathing heavily, freed her of the ropes.

The tired beaters loaded into the launches and drew away a little. At first Jumbo did nothing but stand. Then she seemed to come to her senses, realised she was on her own, and with a little skip turned towards the mainland jungle. There were groans as she disappeared into the bush. After a minute she reappeared. She seemed to have got the scent of her mother and there were further groans as she made to enter the water again to get back to the island. But the lake was too much for her. She stopped, turned back, stood irresolute on the bank and— just like a baby—yelled.

As darkness curtained the lake, we chugged back to camp feeling hot, dusty, scratched and tired out. We had to return to the island at a later date for the impala and other creatures that had still to be rescued.

(*From* "Operation Noah" *by* CHARLES LAGUS)

INTERESTING FACTS ON
HYDRO-ELECTRIC SCHEMES

1. Electricity generated by water power is used in practically every country in the world. Some countries, like Canada, New Zealand, Switzerland, Scotland, and the Scandinavian countries, have an abundant supply of water which makes hydro-electric schemes easier to operate, but in dry, flat countries artificial means of storing and raising water have to be used. Engineers seek to trap as much water as they can in order to get sufficient force to drive a *turbine*. This is a type of water-wheel, consisting of curved blades on a central axis, which is turned by the rushing water. The idea of using the energy in mountain torrents to drive turbines was first adopted by a French paper manufacturer, Aristide Berges, in 1869.

2. A good example of the use of water power is at *Loch Sloy* in Scotland. The original small loch was in a valley high above the beautiful Loch Lomond. This small loch was dammed at one end and, by draining several nearby valleys, the level of the loch was raised. Pipes carry the water down to the power-house. The descending water turns the blades of the turbines which in turn drive the *dynamos*. The electricity thus generated is carried by overhead wires to all parts of the country where, its voltage reduced, it is used in homes and factories.

3. At *Kitimat*, in the Rocky Mountains of British Columbia, the River Nechako had to be turned round through the mountains from east to west, instead of west to east, in order to obtain sufficient water for the reservoir. This hydro-electric scheme was created to provide electric power for the huge factories engaged in the smelting of aluminium. Two tunnels, down which a train could be driven, and ten miles in length, had to be bored through a mountain to join the reservoir with the power-house. There is electric power to spare at Kitimat and this is being used to attract new industries to the Pacific coast of Canada.

4. Hydro-electric plants also play a great part in the industrial progress of Eastern Canada. The natural fall of water at *Niagara*, with its reservoir of the Great Lakes behind it, allows many power-houses to be built at the base of the falls. Further north, the *Saint Lawrence Seaway* has been adapted for power at Shawninigan, near Montreal, and this, together with the hydro-station at Arvida, provides the electrical power needs for much of the industry of the province of Quebec.

5. In the United States of America, the *Tennessee Valley Authority* created dams and power-stations to control and use the waters of the Tennessee River. Their schemes were so successful that land and industries were acquired and the result was that this area was turned into one of the most prosperous farming and industrial districts in the country. On the border of Arizona and Nevada was built the huge *Hoover (Boulder) Dam*. Each spring the Colorado River used to run wild. The winter's snow from the Rockies melted and the river would overflow its banks to flood farmlands and cities, while in summer there would not be enough water. Now the river is regulated to supply households and factories with electricity as well as water for irrigation.

6. One of the most remarkable dams in the world is the *Aswan Dam* in Southern Egypt. Its great walls hold up the flood waters of the River Nile which are released as required through sluice gates to maintain, during the dry season, a flow through the irrigation canals of Egypt. A hydro-electric power-station is now being built on to the dam. This scheme has meant that barren desert wastes are now cultivated, and that thousands of people, who might otherwise have starved, have plenty of food and work.

7. Because of its cheapness, countries with many industries, like Russia, try to obtain as much water-power as they can. On the *River Dneiper*, which flows into the Black Sea, a great dam has been constructed, and this not only provides electricity, but has made the upper part of the Dneiper navigable for river traffic. The Russians also have a large generating station on the bend of the *River Volga* at Kuibishev.

8. In hot, dry countries rivers are usually a blessing, but some have proved disastrous because of flooding. In China the *Yellow River*, which was called " China's Sorrow " because of the number of people drowned each year, has been controlled by dams and its turbulence converted for electrical and irrigation purposes. The completely automatic hydro-station at *Kuanting* provides electricity for China at one third of the cost of steam-driven machines.

9. India has also benefited greatly from such schemes, the *Canada Dam* in Bengal and the *Hirakud Dam* at Orissa being among the largest in the world. The high dam on the River Sutlej in the Punjab towers over 750 feet to span the *Bhakra Gorge*. This latest Indian project provides, in addition to electric power, irrigation for an area greater than Holland.

10. In Australia the flow of the *Snowy River* was diverted to join the sources of other three rivers, Murray, Murrumbidgee and Tumut, for a huge hydro scheme in the Snowy Mountains. This project not only brought an abundance of cheap electrical power, but also supplied much-needed water for the dry western plains and fruit farms of New South Wales and Victoria.

New Zealand, too, has made good use of her natural resources. The *Karapiro Station* in the North Island uses the waters of the Waikato with its reservoir at Lake Taupo. In the South Island, the River Clutha provides electricity at the *Roxburgh Dam*. These two stations, with several other smaller units, supply New Zealand with power and light, so that the lack of coal in the country is not as serious a problem as it might have been.

QUESTIONS ON THE STORY

1. On what river was the Kariba Dam built ?
2. What is the length of this river ?
3. What industry would benefit greatly from the power provided by the Kariba Dam ?
4. Why were the tribesmen around Kariba removed and where were they taken ?
5. Why was time an important factor in the rescue of the animals ?
6. From what book has this story of Kariba been taken ?
7. Can you think of a reason for the extraordinary title of this book ?
8. Name the three men in charge of the expedition to Elephant Island.
9. How did they propose to bring the elephants to the mainland ?
10. How does an elephant swim ?
11. Why did the rescuers approach the island from the leeside ?
12. How many elephants were marooned on the island ?
13. Why was the presence of the baby elephants considered an added danger ?
14. What problem faced the mother elephant when the babies reached the end of the island ?
15. Describe the drive and account for the failure of the first plan.
16. Give an outline of the second plan.
17. In what way did the rising lake help the second plan ?
18. Tell how the young elephant was caught and tied.
19. What did the young elephant do after the rescuers had left her on the mainland ?
20. Why did the rescuers have to return later to Elephant Island ?

QUESTIONS ON THE INTERESTING FACTS

1. (a) Name three countries where hydro-electric schemes are easy to operate.
    (b) What is a " turbine " ?
    (c) Who first used mountain water to produce electricity ?
2. (a) Name a water-power scheme in Scotland.
    (b) By what means is the electrical power carried to homes and factories ?
3. (a) For what purpose was the Kitimat Scheme created ?
    (b) What had to be done to the River Nechako ?
4. (a) Name two hydro-electric stations in Eastern Canada.
    (b) What constitutes the reservoir for the Niagara power-stations ?
5. (a) What work is done by the Tennessee Valley Authority ?
    (b) What river does the Hoover Dam control ?
6. (a) On what river is the Aswan Dam situated ?
    (b) Why is this dam of great benefit to the Egyptian people ?
7. (a) What extra value had the Dneiper Dam, besides producing electricity ?
    (b) On what river is there another great Russian power-station ?
8. (a) Why was the Yellow River called " China's Sorrow " ?
    (b) In what way was the Kuanting power-station different from others ?
9. (a) Where is the Canada Dam ?
    (b) In what district of India is the Bhakra Gorge Dam ?
10. (a) What Australian states are being served by the Snowy Mountains Hydro-Scheme ?

(*b*) Why is hydro-electric power of immense value to New Zealand ?

DEVELOPMENT EXERCISES

1. Point out on the map of the world
   (*a*) Where each of the dams mentioned is situated.
   (*b*) British Columbia, Yellow River, Zimbabwe, Black Sea, the North Island, River Nile, New South Wales, Bengal, Tennessee River, Great Lakes.
2. EITHER (*a*) If you were photographing the rescue of the elephants for television, which shots would you consider the best ?
   OR (*b*) Which would you prefer to use, gas or electricity ? Give reasons for your choice.
3. (*a*) An elephant trumpets. What sounds are made by the following animals (1) donkey ; (2) hyena ; (3) monkey ; (4) pig ; (5) wolf ?
   (*b*) What human characteristics are indicated in the following three sentences ? (1) He has a hide like an elephant. (2) He danced around like an elephant. (3) He has a memory like an elephant.
4. Aristide Berges was the first to use waterfalls for electric power. Find out who invented (*a*) the steam-engine ; (*b*) the gramophone ; (*c*) wireless ; (*d*) the miner's safety-lamp ; (*e*) television.
5. The young elephant is described as being in a similar situation to that of "Gulliver". Who was Gulliver and who made him famous ?
6. A reservoir is used for storing water. What name is given to the store for each of the following : (*a*) grain ; (*b*) aeroplanes ; (*c*) books ; (*d*) gas ; (*e*) guns ?
7. Make a list of all the household uses of electricity.
8. (*a*) Water-power is a compound word. Explain the meaning of the following compounds that include the word "water" : (1) watermark ; (2) waterbiscuit ; (3) water-polo ; (4) watercolours ; (5) waterproof.

    (*b*) Explain each of the following sentences :
        (1) Tom poured oil on troubled waters.
        (2) She threw cold water on the plan.
        (3) It was enough to make one's mouth water.
        (4) Still waters run deep.
        (5) Jim said he would go through fire and water
           for her.

THE SPECTACLED ROADMAN

Richard Hannay, a South African, who is the main character in John Buchan's famous novel, "The Thirty-Nine Steps", is being pursued by the police and a group of foreign spies for a murder which he did not commit. He escapes from London to Galloway in the south of Scotland and in this episode, he assumes the disguise of a roadman who has gone home sick.

MY toilet complete, I took up the barrow and began my journeys to and from the quarry a hundred yards off.

I remember an old scout in Rhodesia once telling me that the secret of playing a part was to think yourself into it. You could never keep it up, he said, unless you could manage to convince yourself that you were it. So I shut off all other thoughts and switched them on to the road-mending. I thought of the little white cottage as my home and made my mind dwell lovingly on sleep in a box-bed.

Now and then a sheep wandered off the heather to stare at me. A heron flapped down to a pool in the stream and started to fish, taking no more notice of me than if I had been a milestone. On I went, trundling my loads of stone, with the heavy step of a professional. Soon I grew warm, and the dust on my face changed into solid and abiding grit.

Suddenly a crisp voice spoke from the road, and looking up I saw a little Ford two-seater, and a round-faced young man in a bowler hat.

"Are you Alexander Turnbull?" he asked. "I am the new County Road Surveyor. You live at Blackhopefoot, and have charge of the section from Laidlaw-byres to the Riggs? Good! A fair bit of road, Turnbull, and not badly engineered. A little soft about a mile off and the edges want cleaning. See you look after that. Good-morning. You'll know me the next time you see me."

Clearly my get-up was good enough for the Surveyor. I went on with my work, and as the morning grew towards noon, I was cheered by a little traffic. A baker's van breasted the hill, and sold me a bag of ginger biscuits which I stowed in my trousers pocket against emergencies. Then a shepherd passed with sheep and disturbed me by asking loudly, "What has become o' Specky?" "In bed with the colic," I replied, and the shepherd passed on.

Just about midday a big car stole down the hill, glided past and drew up a hundred yards beyond. Its three occupants descended as if to stretch their legs and sauntered towards me.

Two of the men I had seen before from the window of the Galloway inn—one lean, sharp and dark, the other comfortable and smiling. The third had the look of a countryman—a vet, perhaps, or a small farmer. He was dressed in ill-cut knicker-bockers, and the eye in his head was as bright and wary as a hen's.

"'Morning," said the last. "That's a fine easy job o' yours."

I had not looked up on their approach, and now, when accosted, I slowly and painfully straightened my back, after the manner of roadmen; spat vigorously after the manner of the low Scot; and regarded them steadily before replying. I confronted three pairs of eyes that missed nothing.

"There's worse jobs and there's better," I said feelingly. "I would rather have yours, sittin' a' day on those cushions. It's you and your cars that wreck my roads. If we a' had our rights, you should be made to mend what you break."

The bright-eyed man was looking at the newspaper lying beside Turnbull's bundle.

"I see you get your papers in good time," he said.

I glanced at it casually. "Aye, in good time, seeing that that paper came out last Saturday, I'm just six days late."

He picked it up, glanced at it and laid it down again. One of the others had been looking at my boots, and a word in German called the speaker's attention to them.

"You've fine taste in boots," he said. "These were never made by a country shoemaker."

"They were not," I said readily. "They were made in London. I got them from the gentleman that was here last year for the shooting. What was his name now?" And I scratched a forgetful head.

Again the sleek one spoke in German. "Let us get on," he said. "This fellow is all right."

They asked one last question.

"Did you see any one pass early this morning? He might be on a bicycle or he might be on foot."

I very nearly fell into the trap and told a story of a cyclist hurrying past in the grey dawn. But I had the sense to see my danger. I pretended to consider very deeply.

"I wasn't up very early," I said. "You see, my daughter was married last night and we stayed up late. Since I came up here there has just been the baker and the Ruchill herd, besides you gentlemen."

One of them gave me a cigar, which I smelt gingerly and stuck in Turnbull's bundle. They got into their car and were out of sight in three minutes.

My heart leaped with an enormous relief, but I went on wheeling my stone. It was as well, for ten minutes later the car returned, one of the occupants waving a hand to me. Those gentry left nothing to chance.

The next step was what puzzled me. I could not keep up this road-making business for long. I had a notion that the cordon was still tight round the glen, and that if I walked in any direction I should meet with questioners.

I stayed at my post till about five o'clock. By that time I had resolved to go down to Turnbull's cottage at nightfall and take my chance of getting over the hills in the darkness. But suddenly a new car came up the road and slowed down a yard or two from me. A fresh wind had risen, and the occupant wanted to light a cigarette.

It was a touring car, with the tonneau full of an assortment of baggage. One man sat in it, and by an amazing chance I knew him. His name was Marmaduke Jopley, and he was an offence to creation. "Marmie" was a familiar figure, I understood, at balls and polo-weeks and country-houses. He was a scandalmonger whom I met in London through a business introduction to his firm. He showed off at a great rate, and pattered about his

duchesses till the snobbery of the creature turned me sick.

Anyhow there he was now, nattily dressed, in a fine new car, obviously on his way to visit some of his smart friends. A sudden daftness took me, and in a second I had jumped into the tonneau and had him by the shoulder.

"Hullo, Jopley," I sang out. "Well met, my lad!"

He got a horrid fright. His chin dropped as he stared at me. "Who are you?" he gasped.

"My name's Hannay," I said. "From Rhodesia, you remember."

"Good heavens, the murderer!" he choked.

"Just so, and there'll be a second murder, if you don't do as I tell you. Give me that coat of yours. That cap, too."

He did as he was bid, for he was blind with terror. I put on his smart driving-coat, stuck the cap on my head and added his gloves to my get up. The dusty roadman in a minute was transformed into one of the neatest motorists in Scotland. On Mr. Jopley's head I clapped Turnbull's unspeakable hat, and told him to keep it there.

Then with some difficulty I turned the car. My plan was to go back the road he had come, for the watchers,

having seen it before, would probably let it pass unre-
marked.

"Now, my child," I said, "sit quite still and be a good
boy. I mean you no harm, I'm only borrowing your
car for an hour or two. But if you play me any tricks, and
above all, if you open your mouth, I'll wring your neck."

I enjoyed that evening's ride. We ran eight miles
down the valley, through a village or two, and I could
not help noticing several strange-looking folk lounging
by the roadside. One touched his cap in salute, and I
responded graciously.

I turned up a side glen which, as I remember from the
map, led into an unfrequented corner of the hills. Presently
we came to a lonely moor, where the night was blacken-
ing the sunset gleam in the bog pools. Here we stopped,
and I obligingly reversed the car and restored to Mr.
Jopley his belongings.

"A thousand thanks," I said. "There's more use in
you than I thought. Now be off and find the police."

As I sat on the hillside, watching the tail lights dwindle,
I reflected on the various kinds of crime I had now
sampled. Contrary to general belief, I was not a murderer
but I had told utter lies, I was a shameless impostor
and a highwayman with a marked taste for expensive
motor-cars.

(*From* "The Thirty Nine Steps" *by* JOHN BUCHAN.)

QUESTIONS ON THE STORY

1. Who is telling the story?
2. Why is he disguised as a road-mender?
3. What advice had the Rhodesian scout given him?
4. Who was the first person to meet him?
5. What was the real road-mender's name?
6. Why did Hannay buy biscuits from the baker?
7. Who recognised that he was not the real road-mender?
8. Describe the foreign agents.
9. Name two ways in which the spies tried to discover if he was really a road-mender.
10. What reason did Hannay give for not seeing anyone early in the morning?
11. In what way did the spies try to make sure that he was a roadman?
12. Why did Hannay not leave the job after they had gone away?
13. What did he intend to do?
14. What caused him to change his plans?
15. Why did Hannay despise Jopley?
16. What did Hannay threaten to do if Jopley did not do as he was told?
17. Why did Hannay take Jopley back the way he came?
18. Whom did they pass on the road?
19. Where did he finally leave Jopley?
20. What crimes had Hannay now sampled?

DEVELOPMENT EXERCISES

1. Point out the train route from London to Galloway.
2. EITHER *(a)* Tell in your own words of the meeting between Hannay and the foreign spies.
   OR *(b)* Detail briefly Jopley's story to the police.
3. Hannay was disguised as a roadmender. What name is given to one who mends *(a)* windows; *(b)* motor cars; *(c)* spectacles; *(d)* furniture; *(e)* boots and shoes?
4. Sheep are grouped in a flock. What is the collective name for each of the following groups *(a)* wolves; *(b)* horses; *(c)* geese; *(d)* pups; *(e)* monkeys?
5. The Road Surveyor came up in a Ford car. Make a list of all the different makes of car that you know, arranging them according to country of origin.
6. The roadman used a barrow. In what job would each of the following be used *(a)* spanner; *(b)* cleaver; *(c)* palette; *(d)* handcuffs; *(e)* lancet?
7. An impostor is one who fraudulently impersonates another person. Find out what name is given to each of the following *(a)* one who throws his voice; *(b)* one who signs another's name; *(c)* one who controls another's mind; *(d)* one who imitates another's voice; *(e)* one who takes another's place in a game.
8. The spies used German so that Hannay would not understand what was said between them. Make a list of ways in which secret messages could be passed from one person to another.

A FIGHT WITH A SHARK

The following adaptation from Jules Verne's fantastic tale, "Twenty Thousand Leagues Under The Sea", published in 1870, deals with an exciting encounter with a man-eating shark. In the amazing underwater craft "Nautilus", are three prisoners, Pierre Aronnax, professor of Natural History in Paris, his servant Conseil, and Canadian Ned Land, who was a harpooner in the United States navy. They have little hope of escaping although the mysterious Captain Nemo and his equally mysterious crew, allow them the freedom of the vessel, and indeed, show them the marvels of the kingdom beneath the seas.

WHEN the "Nautilus" returned to the surface at noon, I found that, when the bearings had been taken, we were near the island of Ceylon, that pearl which hangs from the ear of the Indian peninsula.

I went to look in the library for a book giving an account of this island, one of the most fertile on the globe. At this moment Captain Nemo and the mate appeared. The captain glanced at the map, then turned towards me.

"The island of Ceylon," said he, "is celebrated for its pearl fisheries. Would you like to see one of them, M. Aronnax?"

"I should, indeed, Captain."

"Well, that will be easy enough. Only if we see the fisheries we shall not see the fishermen. The annual working of the pearl fisheries has not yet begun. But that does not matter. I will give orders to make for the Gulf of Manaar, where we shall arrive during the night."

The captain said a few words to his first officer, who went out immediately. The "Nautilus" soon returned to her liquid element, and the manometer indicated that we were at a depth of thirty feet.

"Professor," then said Captain Nemo, "there are pearl fisheries in the Bay of Bengal, in the Indian Ocean, in the seas of China and Japan, in the Bay of Panama and the Gulf of California, but nowhere are such results obtained as at Ceylon. We shall arrive a little too soon, no doubt. The divers do not assemble till March in the Gulf of Manaar, and there for thirty days they give themselves up to this lucrative employment. There are about three hundred boats, and each boat has ten rowers and ten divers. These divers, divided into two groups, plunge into the sea alternately, diving to a depth of about thirteen yards by means of a heavy stone, which they hold between their feet, and a cord fastened to the boat."

"Then," said I, "this primitive method is still in use?"

"Yes," answered Captain Nemo, "although these fisheries belong to the most industrious nation in the world, to England."

"It seems to me, however, that a diving dress, such as you use, would be of great service in such an operation."

"Yes, for the unfortunate divers cannot remain long under the water. An Englishman Percival, in his voyage to Ceylon, does speak of a Caffre, who remained five minutes without rising to the surface, but I can hardly believe it. I know there are some divers, who can stay under for fifty-seven seconds, and some as long as eighty-seven, but these cases are rare, and when the poor creatures return to the boats they bleed from ears and nose. I believe the usual time that divers can stay under is thirty-seconds, and during this time they hasten to fill a small bag with pearl oysters. Divers do not live to be old, however."

"You and your companions," said the captain, "shall see the oyster bank of Manaar, and if by chance some early diver should be found there, we shall see him at work."

"Agreed, Captain."

"But, M. Aronnax, you are not afraid of sharks?"

"I confess, Captain, that I am not yet quite at home with that kind of fish."

"We are used to them," answered Captain Nemo, "and in time you will be so also. However, we shall be armed, and on the road we may have a shark-hunt. So goodbye till tomorrow, sir, and early in the morning."

Next day, Captain Nemo accompanied me to the central staircase, which led to the platform. Ned and Conseil were there, delighted at the notion of the pleasure party which was being prepared. Five sailors from the "Nautilus", oars in hand, awaited us in the boat, which had been made fast against the side. Soon the boat neared Manaar Island; Captain Nemo rose from his seat and watched the sea. Under the dark waters stretched the oyster-bank, an inexhaustible field of pearls, the length of which is more than twenty miles.

At a sign the anchor was dropped, though it had but a little distance to fall, for it was scarcely more than a yard to the bottom, and this was one of the highest points of the oysterbank.

"In a month," said Captain Nemo, "numerous boats will be assembled here, and these are the waters that the divers explore so boldly. This bay is well placed for the purpose; it is sheltered from the high winds, the sea is never very rough here which is highly favourable for divers' work. We will now put on our diving dresses and begin our investigations."

Aided by the sailors, I began to put on my heavy dress. Captain Nemo and my two companions also dressed themselves. None of the sailors of the "Nautilus" were to accompany us.

"Our weapons?" I asked, "our guns?"

"Guns! What for? Do not the mountaineers attack the bear dagger in hand, and is not steel surer than lead? Here is a stout blade; put it in your belt and we will start."

I looked at my companions. They were armed like us, and more than this, Ned Land brandished an enormous harpoon which he had put into the boat before leaving the "Nautilus".

Then, following the example of the captain, I let them put on my heavy copper helmet, and the air reservoirs were at once put into activity. Directly afterwards we were landed in about five feet of water upon a firm sand. Captain Nemo gave us a sign with his hand. We followed him, and going down a gentle slope, we disappeared under the waves. We were on the bank where the pearl oysters breed by the millions. These precious molluscs adhered to the rocks, strongly fastened to them by brown-coloured byssus that prevents them moving.

We walked separately, stopping or going on according to our pleasure. Conseil joined me, and placing his glass plate next to mine, gave me a friendly salutation with his eyes. Ten minutes later, Captain Nemo suddenly stopped. I thought he was making a halt before going back. But no; with a gesture he ordered us to squat down near him. He was pointing and I looked attentively. The uneasy idea of sharks came into my mind, but I was mistaken, and this time we had not to do with any oceanic monster. It was a man, a living man, an Indian, a diver, a poor fellow, no doubt, come to glean before the harvest. I perceived the bottom of his canoe anchored at some feet above his head.

The diver did not see us. The shadow of the rock hid us from him. Besides, how could a poor Indian ever suppose that men, beings like him, were there under the water, watching his movements and losing no detail

of his work? He went up and plunged again several times. He did not bring up more than ten at each plunge, for he was obliged to tear them from the bank. And how many of these oysters for which he risked his life were destitute of pearls!

I watched him with profound attention. All at once, at the moment when the Indian was kneeling on the ground, I saw him make a movement of terror, get up and spring to remount to the surface of the waves.

I understood this fear. A gigantic shadow appeared above the unfortunate plunger. It was an enormous shark advancing diagonally, with eyes on fire and open jaws. I was mute with terror, incapable of making a movement.

The voracious monster, with a vigorous stroke of his fin, was springing towards the Indian who threw himself on one side and avoided the bite of the shark, but not the stroke of his tail, for that tail, striking him on the chest, stretched him on the ground.

This scene had hardly lasted some seconds. The shark returned to the charge, and turning on his back, it was prepared to cut the Indian in two when I felt Captain Nemo, who was near me, suddenly rise, the dagger in his hand. The shark perceived his fresh adversary, and, going over on its stomach again, directed itself rapidly towards him.

I still see the attitude of Captain Nemo. Thrown backwards, he was waiting the formidable shark with admirable courage, and when it threw itself upon him he turned on one side and thrust his dagger into its stomach. But that was not the end. A terrible combat took place. The shark reddened, so to speak, and blood flowed in streams from its wounds. The sea was dyed red and I saw no more until it cleared a little and I perceived the audacious captain holding on to one of the fins, struggling hand to hand with the monster, belabouring its body with dagger thrusts without being able to reach the heart, where blows are mortal.

I looked on with haggard eyes and saw the phases of the struggle change. The captain fell on the ground, overthrown by the enormous mass that was bearing him down. The jaws of the shark opened and all would have been over for the captain, if, harpoon in hand, Ned Land, rushing towards the shark, had not struck it

with its terrible point. The waves were agitated by the movements of the shark that beat them with indescribable fury. Ned Land had not missed his aim. It was the death-rattle of the monster.

In the meantime Ned Land had set free the captain, who rose unhurt, went straight to the Indian, quickly cut the cord which fastened him to the stone, took him in his arms and with a vigorous kick, he went up to the surface of the sea. We all three followed him and in a short time we reached the diver's boat.

Captain Nemo's first care was to recall the unfortunate man to life. I did not know if he would succeed, for the blow from the shark's tail might have killed him. Happily, under the vigorous friction of Conseil and the captain, I saw the drowned man gradually recover his senses. He opened his eyes. What must have been his surprise, terror even, at seeing four large brass heads leaning over him! Above all, what must he have thought, when Captain Nemo, drawing from a pocket in his garment a bag of pearls, put it into his hand! This magnificent gift from the man of the sea to the poor Indian of Ceylon was accepted by him with a trembling hand. His frightened eyes showed that he did not know to what superhuman beings he owed his fortune and his life.

At a sign from the captain we went back to the oyster bank and following the road we had already come along, half an hour's walking brought us to the anchor that fastened the boat of the "Nautilus" to the ground.

Once embarked, we each, with the help of the sailors, took off our heavy helmets. Captain Nemo's first word was for the Canadian.

"Thank you, Land," he said.

"I owed it to you, Captain," answered Ned Land.

A pale smile glided over the captain's lips and that was all.

"To the 'Nautilus'," he said.

Soon we were back on board.

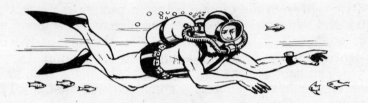

INTERESTING FACTS ABOUT UNDERWATER LIFE

1. An amazing part of Jules Verne's story is that he tells the underwater adventures of a submarine before submarines were invented. His book was published in 1870 and the first successful submarine was made by a Swedish engineer, *Nordenfelt*, in 1885. Another man who, like Verne, seemed to read the future was the famous Italian painter *Leonardo da Vinci*, who made drawings and designs of aeroplanes, almost 400 years before they were invented. The writer H. G. Wells, who wrote "The Invisible Man" and "The First Man on the Moon" may also have prophesied in these books what will one day come to pass.

2. The name *"Nautilus"* comes from the Greek word "nautilos" meaning a sailor. There is a shellfish called a nautilus, which has a shell shaped like a horn; it propels itself through the sea by squirting out water. Ancient tradition says that the nautilus had the power of raising its arms and swimming with them. In 1958 the United States naval submarine "Nautilus", was the first atomic-powered submarine to make the historic underwater journey from one side of the North Pole to the other. It went under the ice cap off Point Barrow, Alaska and came up four days later in the Greenland Sea.

3. Nearly seven tenths of the earth's surface is covered with water. The greatest sea depths are to be found in the Atlantic Ocean (*Challenger Ridge*) and the Pacific Ocean

(*Japan Trench*). Round the countries of the world, the land shelves gradually to a depth of 600 feet below the level of the sea and then descends more steeply to the sea-bed. This underwater apron, which extends for many miles from dry land is called the *continental shelf* and it forms the limit of the areas in which fishermen usually work.

4. In speaking of depths of water, sailors use the term "*fathom*" which equals six feet. The earliest way of finding depths was by a sailor throwing a measured rope with a lead attached over the side of the ship. This was known as "heaving or *swinging the lead*", and, as the sailor appeared to be doing nothing, the modern phrase "swinging the lead" is applied to a person who is apparently idle. The modern method of obtaining depths is by an *echo-sounding* device. Sound waves are timed on their way to the ocean floor, from which they are reflected back to the ship. It is even possible to detect shoals of fish by this method.

5. Fish from the sea provide much of the food for the countries of the world. *Trawlers* and *drifters* operate in distant fishing grounds to bring back the harvest of fish; these fish can be smoked, salted, canned or preserved, so as to reach people who live far from the sea, in good condition. *Whaling* ships work in the Antarctic Ocean, the only area where these great sea-mammals survive in great numbers. When a whale is spotted, a harpoon gun is fired. The harpoon contains an explosive charge which kills the whale instantly. The whale is "*flensed*" or cut up for oil, meat and bones.

6. Besides fish many useful products are obtained from the sea. *Salt* and *magnesium* are extracted from sea-water while the seaweed around our shores can be useful as a *fertiliser* or as a natural food for sheep. Seaweed is also a valuable source of *iodine*, as well as of a valuable jelly, which is used in the manufacture of tooth-paste and

medical dressings. Anyone who .eats sausages, jellies
ice-cream or lemon-curd is likely to be .eating something
which contains *alginates* or jellies derived from seaweed.

7. Shellfish or molluscs formed an important part of
the daily food in ancient times; in some countries, too,
shells were used as personal ornaments, and in others,
as a form of money. Most molluscs have one shell but
some have two, like the oyster and the mussel, in which
case whey are called *bivalves.* The common oysters
round the British Isles line their shells with *mother-of-pearl,* which is used for knife-handles and ornaments,
while some even produce small pearls. The finest
examples of *pearls,* however, come from the tropical
seas. Such pearls are made by pieces of grit getting into
the oyster; throughout the years these particles are
covered with a milk-white coating called *nacre.*

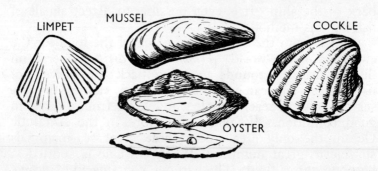

LIMPET   MUSSEL   COCKLE

OYSTER

8. Submarines are ships which steer under water and
fins called *hydroplanes* control the depth to which the
vessel sinks. These hydroplanes are adjusted so that the
submarine travels at an even depth. When only a little
below sea-level, a *periscope* can be raised, allowing those
in the submarine to see everything on the surface without
the submarine itself being seen. Formerly, submarines
could only remain under water for a short time, but a

"*schnorkel*" or breathing tube, reaching up to the surface from the submarine, allowed this period to be extended. New methods of air-conditioning in a submarine have

been found and the United States nuclear submarine "Triton" was the first to complete a 41,000 mile under-water voyage around the world while submerged. The voyage took 84 days and she followed approximately the course charted by the navigator Ferdinand Magellan in his expedition of 1519-21 when the globe was circled for the first time.

9. A *diver* has an interesting as well as a dangerous job. In addition to keeping a sharp eye out for all kinds of strange creatures which may attack him, he has to guard against going too deep, for the mounting pressure of water could crush him. Natives who dive for oysters and sponges could previously stay down only for a short period, but now these "skin-divers" can stay down for a longer time by the aid of *aqualungs*, which are air cylinders fastened to their backs to help them to breathe under the waves. Light diving suits with breathing apparatus allow "*frogmen*" to carry out underwater salvage for quite a long time. Heavier diving suits with copper helmets and heavy lead boots enable divers to work at great depths.

10. *Diving bells* are huge steel bell-shaped tanks which are used to lay foundations on the sea-bed. They are lowered into the water by huge chains and a connecting pipe supplies air to the occupants. These are mainly used in the construction of piers and bridges. *A bathy-sphere* is a round steel globe with thick quartz windows which can be lowered to great depths. It is used by scientists to study marine life and it is usually equipped with cameras to film the amazing mysteries of the deep.

QUESTIONS ON THE STORY

1. Name the three prisoners in the "Nautilus".
2. Who is telling the story?
3. Near what island was the "Nautilus" cruising?
4. When did the divers fish for pearls each year?
5. What instrument recorded the depths of the submarine?
6. To whom did the Ceylon pearl fisheries belong?
7. Name the places where Captain Nemo said pearls could be found.
8. Describe the manner in which the divers fished for pearls.
9. What was the usual time a diver could stay under water?
10. What sport did Captain Nemo say they might have on the way to the oyster banks?
11. How many went into the small boat?
12. What was the length of the oyster bank?
13. Why was the bay most suitable for pearl fishing?
14. What weapons did Captain Nemo favour for their journey?
15. Why did Captain Nemo halt the party underwater?
16. What had disturbed the Indian's work?
17. Who went to the Indian's rescue?
18. Describe how the shark was finally overcome.
19. How was the diver brought back to life?
20. What did Captain Nemo give to the poor Indian diver?

QUESTIONS ON THE INTERESTING FACTS

1. (a) Why is Jules Verne's story so fantastic?
   (b) Who first designed aeroplanes?
2. (a) What power was the nautilus shell supposed to have?
   (b) What modern vessel has been named "Nautilus"?
   (c) What remarkable feat did it accomplish?
3. (a) Where are the greatest sea-depths to be found?
   (b) Name the deepest sea areas in the world.
   (c) What determines the limit of the fishing grounds?
4. (a) What length is (i) a league; (ii) a fathom?
   (b) How was the depth of water obtained in early days?
   (c) Describe the echo-sounding method of obtaining depths.
5. (a) Name two ways of herring fishing.
   (b) Where are whales mostly found?
   (c) What does "flensed" mean?
6. (a) Name two useful products, besides fish, which are obtained from the sea.
   (b) Name two products from seaweed.
7. (a) For what were shells used in ancient times?
   (b) What is (i) a bivalve; (ii) nacre?
8. (a) What controls the depths to which a submarine sinks?
   (b) What is (i) a periscope; (ii) a schnorkel?
9. (a) Why is a diver's job dangerous?
   (b) Name three types of diver.
10. (a) For what are diving bells used?
    (b) How do scientists study marine life at great depths?

DEVELOPMENT EXERCISES

1. Point out on the map of the world: (a) Ceylon; (b) China; (c) India; (d) Japan; (e) Bay of Bengal; (f) Gulf of California; (g) Bay of Panama; (h) Alaska; (i) Greenland Sea; (j) Antarctic Ocean.

2. EITHER (a) Imagine you are diving for the lost treasure of a Spanish galleon. Give a short account of your experiences.

   OR (b) Tell the story that the Indian diver told to his friends.

3. The manometer was used to measure the depth. In what way are the following connected with measurement: (a) barometer; (b) chronometer; (c) gasometer; (d) perimeter; (e) thermometer?

4. "To swing the lead" is a colloquial expression meaning to avoid work purposely. What do the following phrases mean: (a) to iron out your differences; (b) to steel yourself against a shock ; (c) to haul over the coals; (d) to play with fire; (e) to strike while the iron is hot?

5. Make a list of ladies' ornaments in which pearls are used.

6. Submarine comes from sub = under and maris = the sea. Find out the meanings of: (a) subway; (b) submerge; (c) subordinate; (d) sub-editor; (e) subterranean.

7. Nautilus, the name of a shell, was given to a submarine. Give two different meanings for each of the following: (a) league; (b) bow; (c) sole; (d) reel; (e) plain.

8. "Ceylon, that pearl which hangs from the ear of the Indian peninsula." This is a form of speech called a metaphor, which is a comparison that implies that one thing has the qualities of the other. Complete the following metaphors:

(a) Knowledge is a tree and reading is one of its many————

(b) He was disappointed because his friend had ————his coat.

(c) We did not fall in with their plans because we had————a rat.

(d) I lay awake until Mother Sleep folded me to her————

(e) The newly married couple were————into the sea of matrimony.